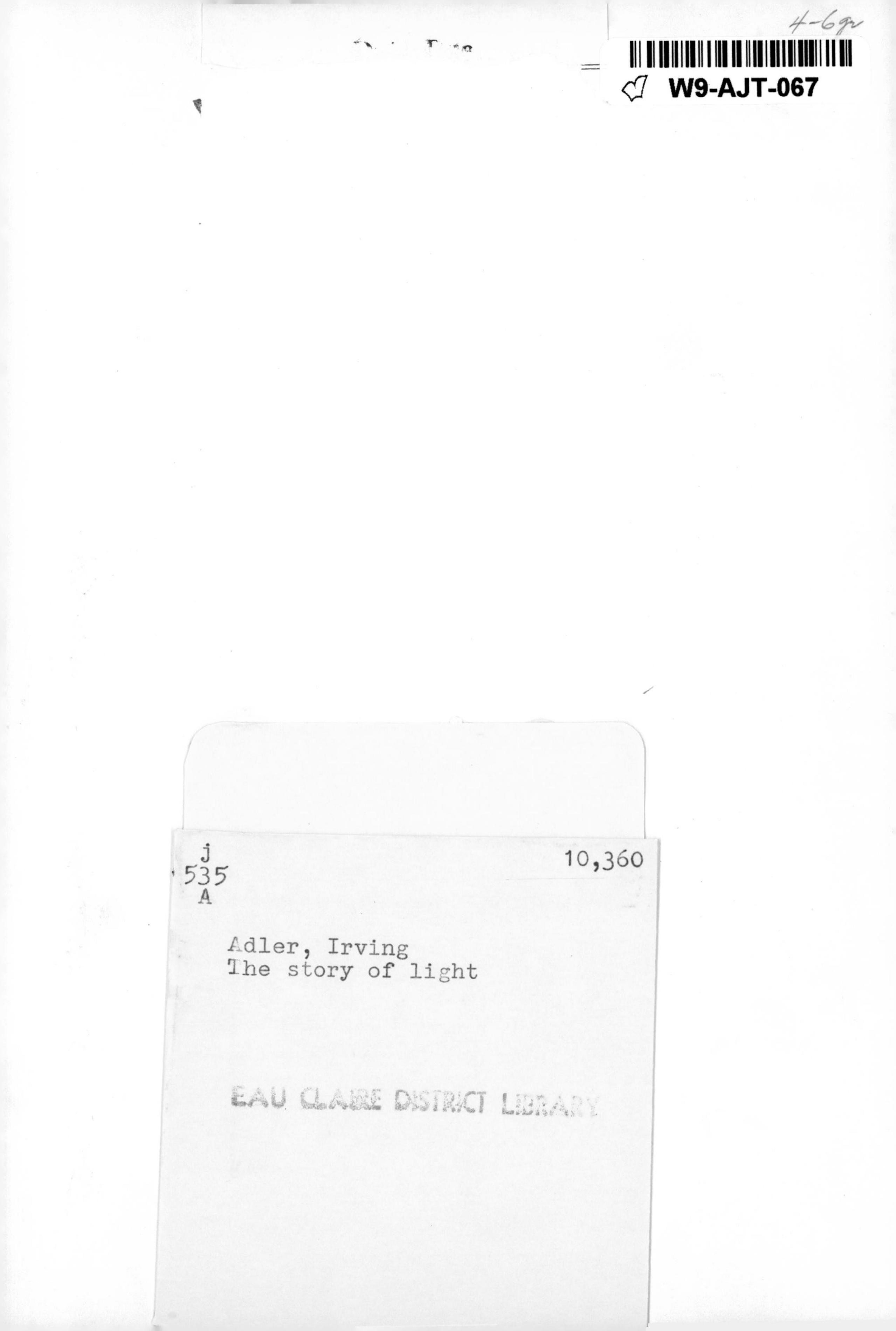

About the Book

With simple experiments and observations, this book creates a fascinating study showing how fast light travels, the tricks it plays, where it comes from, its relation to atomic structure, and how it can be put to work.

Irving Adler writes about light with clarity and interest, starting with ordinary mirrors and lenses and following his subject all the way to the center of the atom.

Anne Lewis's drawing and diagrams amplify the story and add to it a dimension of fun.

The Story of LIGHT

Illustrated by Anne Lewis

The Story of LIGHT

by Irving Adler

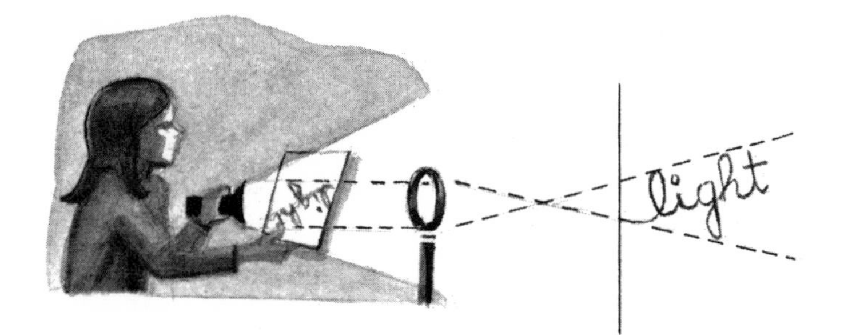

HARVEY HOUSE, INC.
Publishers
Irvington-on-Hudson, New York

To Peggy, Steve, and Roo

Revised Editions, 1965, 1971

Library of Congress Catalog Card Number: 79-93519
Manufactured in the United States of America

HARVEY HOUSE, INC.
Publishers
Irvington-on-Hudson, N.Y. 10533

ISBN 0-8178-4752-9 LIBRARY EDITION

ISBN 0-8178-4751-0 TRADE EDITION

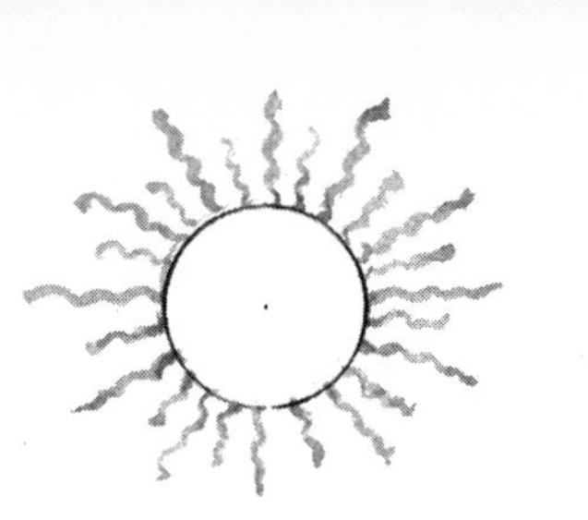

Contents

Everybody's Messenger

This is a book about light. It will tell you interesting facts about many simple, ordinary things like a glass of water, mirrors, soap bubbles, and hot pavements. At the same time it is a story of mystery and adventure. It will unlock the passageway that leads to the center of the atom, exposing its innermost workings.

Parts of this story sound like a fairy tale. But the wonders it describes are all true. This does not make the story any less exciting, for there is no adventure more thrilling than discovering the real wonders of the world we live in.

The Jinni of the Lamp

You have heard about this Jinni before, in the story of Aladdin. Aladdin had a magic lamp, and every time he rubbed the lamp, a Jinni appeared, ready to obey his commands. You, too, can make a Jinni appear, because you also have a magic lamp, the electric-light bulb. Snap the switch, and there he is, the first hero of this story, the Spirit of the Lamp, known as light!

You don't always need a lamp to make the Jinni appear. In fact, during the day, light comes of its own accord with the sun. Then the problem is, not to make it appear, but to make it disappear! Try to shut it out of a room and it streams in through the window pane or wriggles in through the keyhole. Moving picture houses close their doors against it, and photographers build special traps that will keep it out of the dark room.

The Jinni obeyed Aladdin's commands. Will light obey yours? Well, that depends on how much you know. Light obeys only a wise master. You can't hold it by brute force. Grab at it, and it slips through your fingers. If you don't know much about it, it will turn your ignorance against you and play tricks on you. But if you study its habits and learn all its tricks, your knowledge gives you power over it, and you can put it to work. People have learned how to make many things do work for them, from waterfalls to atoms. A

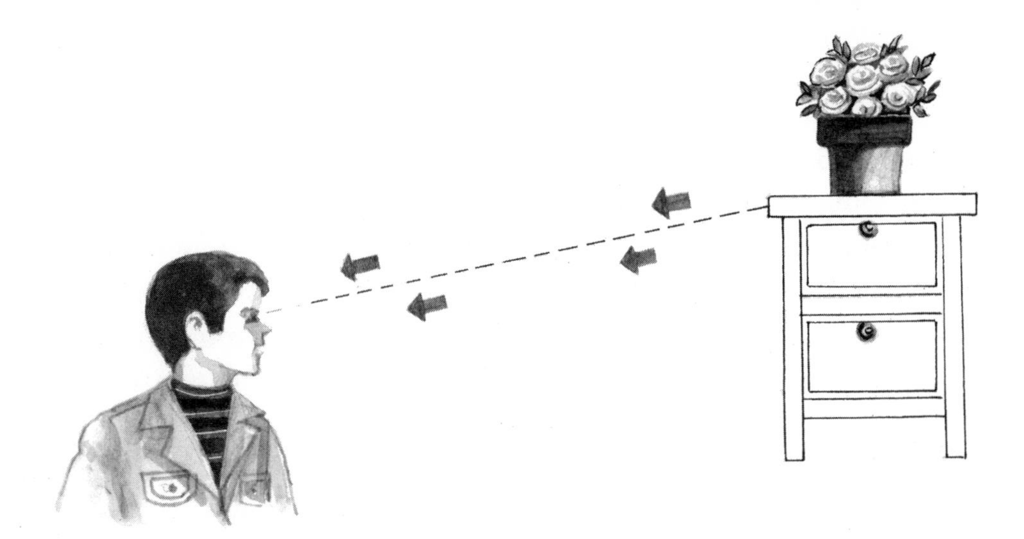

thing's capacity to do work is called its *energy*. There are many kinds of energy, such as motion, heat, electrical energy, and chemical energy. Light, too, is a kind of energy. Does this seem strange to you? As you read this book, you will find the key to unlock this mystery, for the purpose of this book is to introduce you to mankind's knowledge about light and the power that this knowledge has given us.

The Messenger

Did you ever walk through a dark room at night? If you have, then you have certainly discovered a table or other piece of furniture by stubbing your toe against it. Didn't you wish you had known it was there before you hit it! If only it could have sent you a message across space, warning you of its presence! Fortunately for you, it can *when there is light in the room,* for the light serves as everybody's messenger. It travels from the table to you and tells you that the table is there. When you say that you *see* the table, it really means that you have received the light message, with the aid of those special receivers known as *eyes.*

Light is only one of many messengers that we use. Another important one is sound, for which we carry special sound-receivers known as *ears.* Many things send out both sound and light messages at the same time. When you look both ways before crossing a street, you can see and hear the approaching cars. It's good to be able to receive both types of message, because sometimes one of them is blocked and cannot reach you. When a car is coming around a sharp curve, you may not see it, but you can hear it in time to get out of the way. At other times the light message comes through, but the sound does not. For example, looking at a highway in a valley below you, you can frequently see cars moving in the distance, without being able to hear them.

Through Empty Space

An important difference between light and sound is shown by this simple experiment: An electric bell is suspended inside a sealed glass jar. At first the bell is surrounded by the air in the jar. Then the air is pumped out so that the bell will be surrounded by empty space. While the air is in the jar, you can *see* the hammer of the bell strike the gong, and you can *hear* it ring. But after the air is pumped out, even though you can still see the bell, you cannot hear it.

Light can travel through empty space, but sound can travel only when there is something, such as air, through which to travel. We call the air a *material medium.* Water is another material medium for sound. Of course, light, too, can travel through these *media* (plural of medium), but light does not depend upon them to get from place to place. Since the space that separates us from the sun and stars is empty, they cannot send us sound messages, but they can

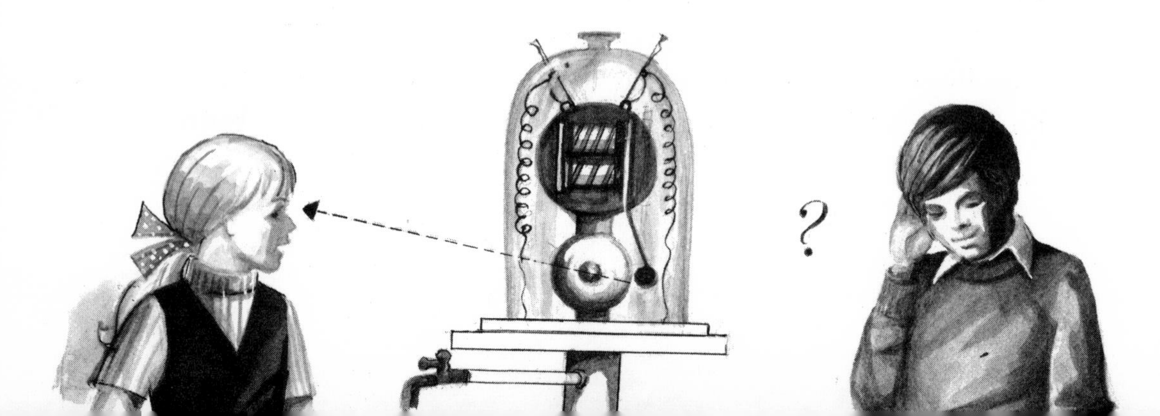

and do send us light. Everything we know about the stars has been learned from the light messages that they send us.

Speed Demon

Out in the country, a quarter of a mile away across an open field, a man is chopping wood. You can see each stroke of the ax, and you can also hear it. But there's something peculiar about this! You see the stroke first, and hear it about a second later! This strange experience shows another important difference between light and sound. Light travels much faster than sound, and that's why the light message reaches you first. Sound travels at a speed of 1100 feet per second. But light travels about a million times as fast, at a speed of 186,000 *miles* per second. At that rate it can travel around the world (a distance of 25,000 miles) in about one-seventh of a second. Sunlight has to travel 93 million miles to reach us, yet it crosses this great distance in about eight minutes. Light is the speediest messenger man will ever have, because it is the fastest thing that moves.

How Far?

When a distant object sends out light and sound messages at the same time, you can use the difference between their speed to find out how far away the object is. A boy saw a skyrocket explode in the air and heard the bang five seconds later. Since light travels so very fast, the boy saw the flash almost at the moment that it happened. Therefore the sound traveled five seconds before it reached him and the distance of the rocket must have been five times 1100 feet, or about one mile.

The next time there is a thunderstorm, you can use the same method for measuring the distance to the center of the storm. The electrical discharges in the clouds send out light messages (lightning) and sound messages (thunder). When you see a flash of lightning, count the number of seconds that pass before you hear the thunder. The distance to the storm will be one mile for every five seconds. An easy way of counting the seconds without a watch is to count slowly "a thousand and one, a thousand and two," and so on.

Playing Tricks

A Riddle

Where will you find trees growing only in pairs, attached to each other, one growing up and the other growing down? On the shore of a lake, of course! One tree is real, and the other is its reflection in the water. This is one of the practical jokes that light is playing all the time, making things seem to be where they aren't. But like any trick, it doesn't fool you once you know how it's done.

When light brings us a message from some object, it gives us a clue to the position of the object. If we look in the direction from which the light comes, we expect to find the object there. But this is where light gets a chance to play tricks. It can give us a misleading clue by changing its direction before it reaches us. One way it can do this is by striking against a smooth surface like the surface of a lake.

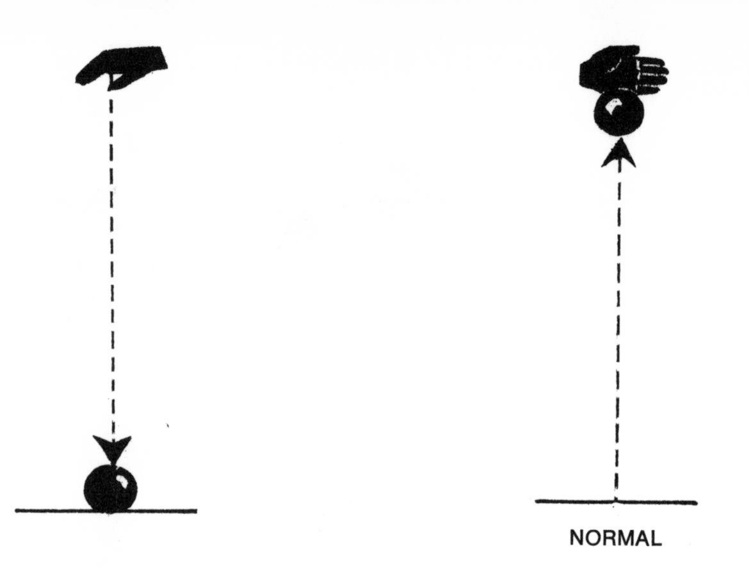

How Light Bounces

Light will bounce off a smooth surface just like a rubber ball. This is called *reflection.* To learn how this happens, try these simple experiments.

Throw a ball directly down onto a smooth floor. The ball will bounce back directly toward you. The path of the ball in this case is a line standing straight up from the floor the way a fence post stands up out of the ground, not leaning one way or the other. This line is called a *normal* to the surface of the floor.

Now throw the ball forward against the floor. After striking the floor this time, it will bounce away from you on the other side of the normal drawn to the point where it struck the floor. The angle between the normal and the path before the bounce is called the *angle of incidence.* The angle between the normal and the path after the bounce is called the *angle of reflection.* If you throw the ball many times, changing the angle of incidence each time, you will notice that, whether it is large or small, *the angle of incidence is always equal to the angle of reflection.*

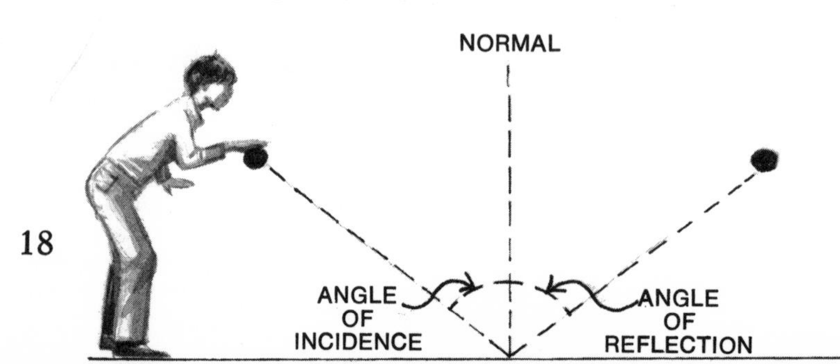

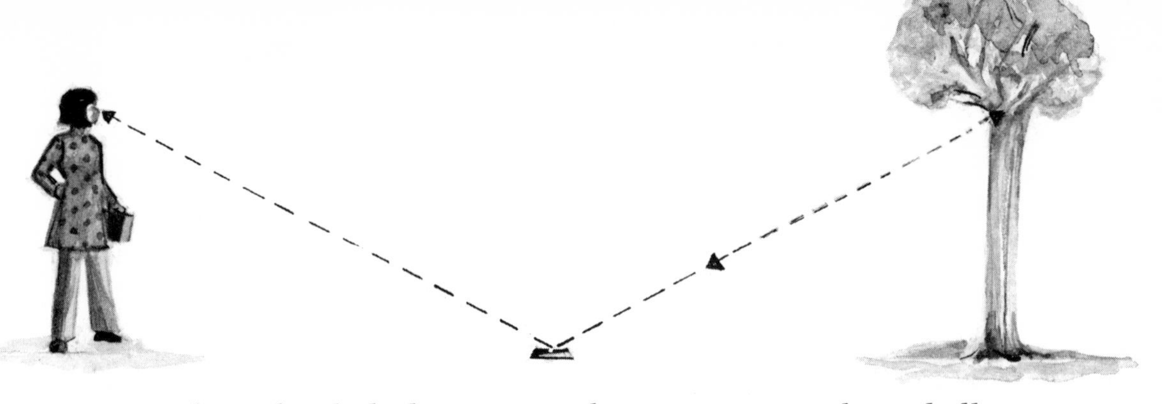

To show that light bounces in the same way, make a chalk mark at your eye level on a tree trunk. Then put a pocket mirror on the ground a few feet from the tree. Walk backward away from the mirror until you see the chalk mark in the mirror. When you do, it means that light coming from the chalk mark has been reflected from the mirror to your eye, as shown in the diagram. That the angle of incidence is equal to the angle of reflection is proved by the fact that you and the tree will be the same distance from the mirror.

Seeing Things Where They Aren't

Now suppose you put a lighted candle in front of a mirror. Some light from the flame comes directly to your eye. You see the flame itself. But some light from the flame reaches your eye *after* striking the mirror. When it bounced back, it changed its direction. Because of this change of direction, this part of the light appears to come from behind the mirror. As a result, it looks as though the candle itself is in back of the mirror. What you see here is called a *virtual image.*

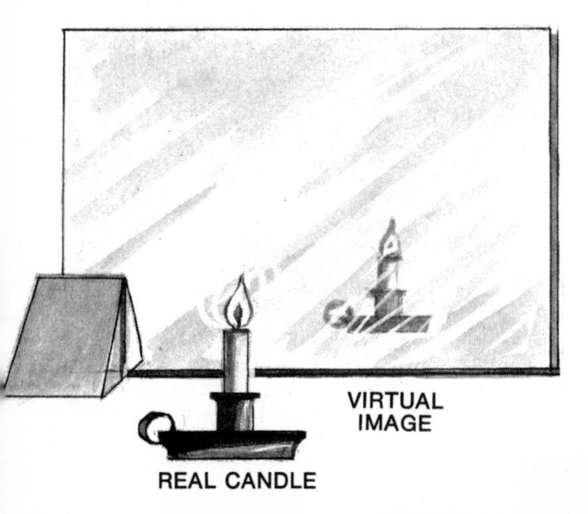

Another simple experiment can help you locate the position of the virtual image. Set a piece of flat, clear glass so that it stands vertically on a table. (Hold it pressed between two book ends or use an empty picture frame that has a stand.) Then place a lighted candle some distance in front of the glass. Enough of the light is reflected to give you a virtual image. Then place another candle on the other side of the glass, moving it from spot to spot until you find the place where it seems to occupy the same space as the virtual image. You will find that both candles will be the same distance from the glass.

The Broken Spoon

Fill a drinking glass with water and put a spoon into it. Now hold it up to your eye level and look at the spoon. The spoon is broken! But don't throw the spoon away. There's nothing really wrong with it. Light is playing tricks again. It has fooled us by changing its direction.

This time the light changed its direction, not by bouncing off a surface, but by passing through a surface from the water into the air. Light generally changes direction when it passes from one medium to another. This kind of bending of light's path is called *refraction.* The light that came from the top of the spoon traveled only through air. Therefore it did not change its direction. But the light that came from the bottom part of the spoon had to pass from the water into the air before reaching your eyes. Therefore, it changed its direction. As a result, the part of the spoon under water looks as though it has moved over a bit; it looks as though it has separated from the top—it looks broken!

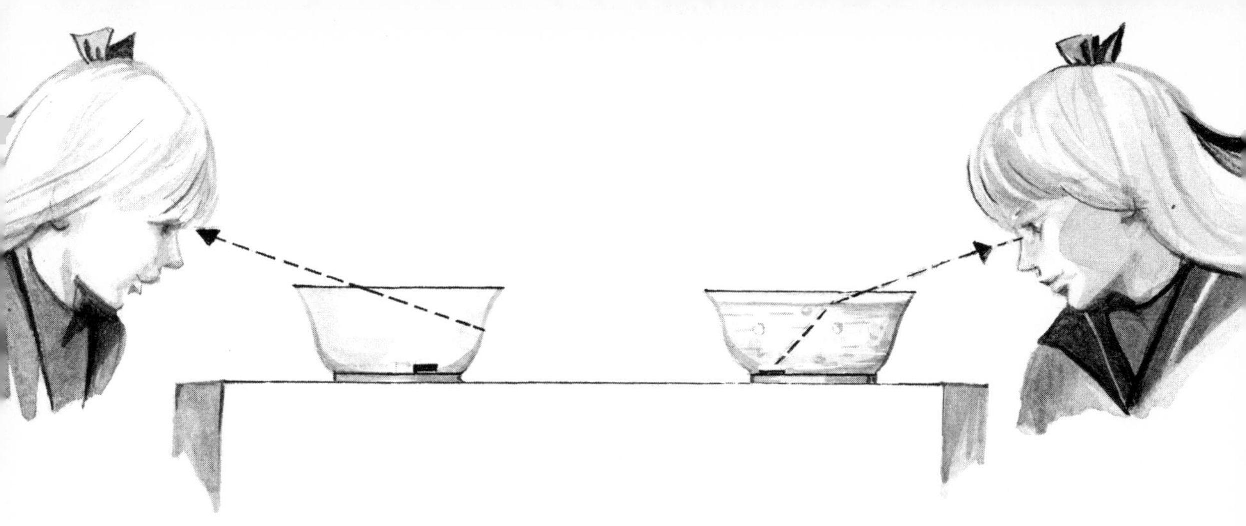

The Mysterious Penny

Now that you know the secret of refraction, you can get light to help you do a very amusing trick. You can make a penny appear out of nowhere by pouring water into a bowl!

Sit down at a table, and put a bowl on the table, far enough away from you so that the bottom of the bowl is hidden from view by the rim. Put a penny inside the bowl. Since the penny rests on the bottom, it will also be invisible. Now slowly pour water into the bowl. As the water level rises, the penny will gradually appear, until all of it is visible on the bottom of the bowl! After you have practiced this trick several times, try it on your friends. But don't let them see you put the penny into the bowl.

Can you explain the trick? The diagram shows you that before you poured the water in, the penny couldn't send you a light message because the rim of the bowl was in the way. But when the bowl was full of water, the bending of the light as it left the surface of the water made it possible for the light to reach your eye. And so you saw the penny.

Next time you step into a brook or a bathtub full of water, look at your feet. They seem to be much closer to your knees than they usually are. Did your legs shrink? No, it's a light trick again. The refraction of the light leaving the water makes everything in the water look higher than it really is.

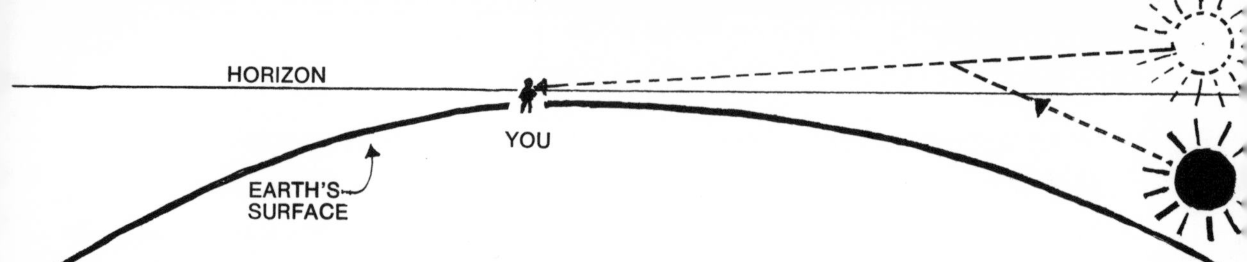

Making Trouble for the Navigator

Navigators of ships and planes check their position by measuring the height of a star above the horizon. Since their only clue to the position of a star is the direction from which the starlight comes, this gives light a chance to play another trick. The air surrounding the earth is dense at the bottom (a lot of it packed into a small space). At higher and higher levels it is more and more rarefied (that is, it is spread out thin so that there's more empty space and less air). Starlight passing through the earth's atmosphere passes through layers of greater and greater air density until it reaches the navigator's eye. But passing from air of low density into air of higher density makes the light bend, just as it did when it passed from the water into the air in the experiments. As a result, the navigator sees the star where it isn't. In order to get its true position, he must always make a correction for refraction. Fortunately, it is possible to figure out what the correction should be, and this is printed in the almanac the navigator uses.

Since the earth is round, some objects on its surface that are far away from you cannot be seen because they are hidden by the bulge. A level line drawn from you is called the horizon. When the sun passes below the horizon, we say it has set. However, for a few minutes after sunset, the sunlight, bent as it passes through the atmosphere, appears to come from above the horizon. So you can actually see the sun after it has set!

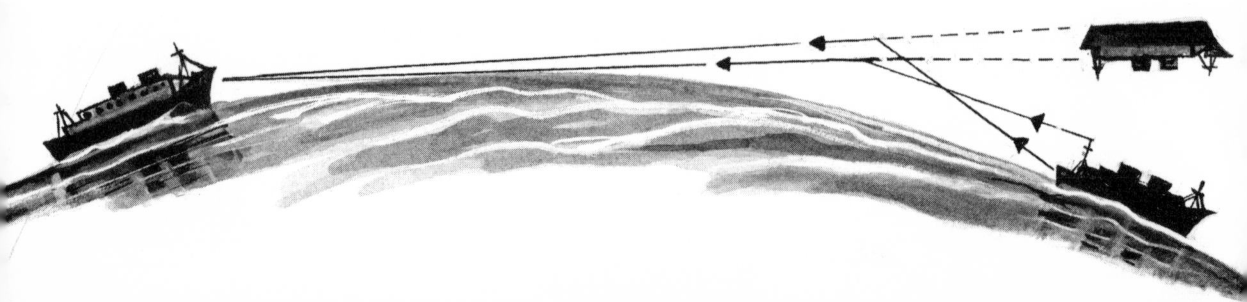

An Arctic navigator, separated from one of his ships, saw the ship far off in the distance, upside down above the horizon! He sailed in that direction and found the ship there, but right side up, of course. What he had seen was a peculiar effect of refraction called *looming*. Because of the very low temperature in the Arctic, the lower layers of air were unusually dense. Light coming from the ship, which was actually below the horizon, was bent into a curve that curved more sharply than the surface of the earth. That's why light was able to reach him, and made the ship seem to be above the horizon. Since rays of light from the bottom of the ship were curved more than rays from the top of the ship, they crossed each other on the way. As a result, the top appeared under the bottom and the ship looked upside down.

The Vanishing Lake

Desert travelers have reported seeing a lake in the distance. Spurred on by heat and thirst, they hurried toward it, only to see it vanish as they approached, and reappear farther on. If you have read the story of Aladdin, you know that the Jinni of the Lamp could carry palaces across whole continents, so you will not be surprised that light can tease travelers by moving a lake. It's a mean trick, but we can let you in on its secret.

First, we have to talk, not about light, but about some media through which light can travel. Water is one such medium, air is another. When a mass of air, like the atmosphere, lies above a body of water, like a lake, we see a boundary that separates them. This is the *surface* of the water—the place where the water ends and the air begins. Now, strange as it may seem, it is also possible to have a surface separating air from air. For example, when a layer of dense, heavy air lies right next to a layer of rarefied, thin air, there is a surface between the two layers.

You also know that the surface of water can reflect light like a mirror. Remember the upside-down trees that you've seen in a still lake? We take that kind of reflection for granted, because we see it all the time. But here is something surprising. The surface between two layers of air can also reflect light in much the same way.

The layer of air close to hot desert sand is superheated, and it becomes more rarefied than the air immediately above it. Light from the distant blue sky, striking the surface of this rarefied air, is reflected to the eye of the traveler. So he sees a patch of blue which seems to come from the desert sand. Of course, the blue really comes from the sky, but it looks exactly like a cool and placid lake.

The Mirage on the Highway

You don't have to go to the desert to see a mirage. You can often see one when you're driving along a concrete highway on a very hot day. The hot pavement does the same thing to the air as the desert sand. As a result, you may see little pools of water appearing and disappearing on the highway. Sometimes you will even see a car far ahead of you upside down, reflected in one of these imaginary pools!

Now let's see just what happens to light when it fools us in this way.

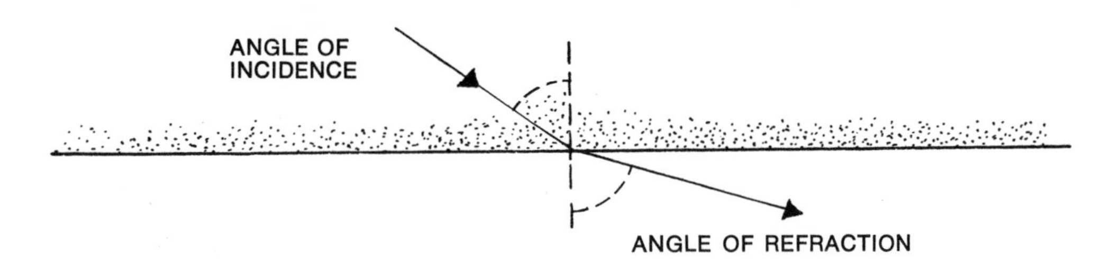

When light strikes the surface between two transparent media, such as air and water or dense air and rarefied air, some of it bounces off and some of it passes through, being bent on the way. (Remember the broken spoon?) The angle between the ray of light and the normal is called the *angle of incidence.* The angle between the normal and the ray as

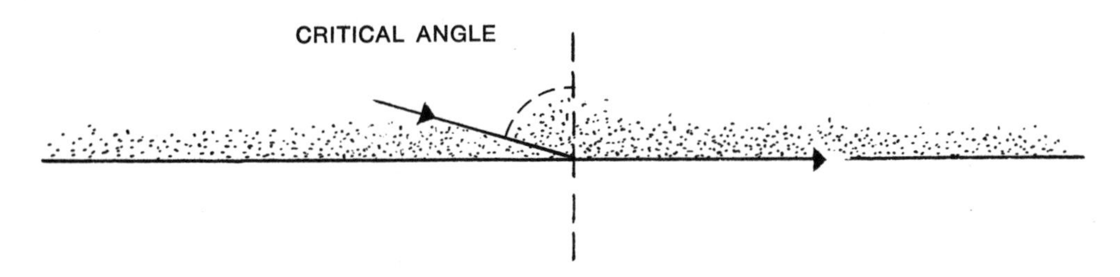

it leaves the surface after passing through is called the *angle of refraction.* When light passes from a dense to a rare, or thin medium, the angle of refraction is larger than the angle of incidence. Now if the angle of incidence is made larger, the angle of refraction becomes larger, too. As the angle increases, the refracted ray comes closer and closer to the surface until it reaches a certain angle of incidence, known as the *critical angle.* At that angle the refracted ray won't pass through the surface, but will run along it instead. *And if the angle of incidence is larger than the critical angle, the ray doesn't pass through the surface at all, but bounces back and is reflected.* When this happens, we say that *total reflection* has taken place. Look at the diagram to see how this works.

TOTAL REFLECTION

A Home-Made Mirage

You can make a mirage yourself by producing total reflection from the surface of water. Fill a tumbler with water and set it near the edge of a table. Put a lighted candle behind the tumbler so that the flame is below the surface of the water. Now bend down slowly and look down at the surface of the water. As you lower your eyes, the flame will disappear completely. None of the light is transmitted through the surface. Now look *up* at the surface of the water from below, and you will see an image of the flame *above* the water level. The light from the flame has undergone total reflection, just as if the surface of the water were a mirror.

Funny Faces

Do you think you have a nice face? Look into a polished brass door knob or any reflecting curved surface, and see for yourself. Like Little Red Riding Hood, you'll have to say, "What big ears you have!" If you come up close, your face will be all nose and no chin! Light is playing a joke on you again. This time the trick lies in the fact that the normals to a curved surface don't all point in the same direction. As a result, rays of light are reflected in peculiar ways depending on how the surface is curved, and a distorted image is produced. Amusement houses take advantage of this trick of light by setting up curved mirrors of all sorts. Look into one, and you see yourself as Humpty Dumpty. Look into another, and you look like the Thin Man in the circus.

Now that the jokes are getting personal, it's time to stop playing around, and put light to work.

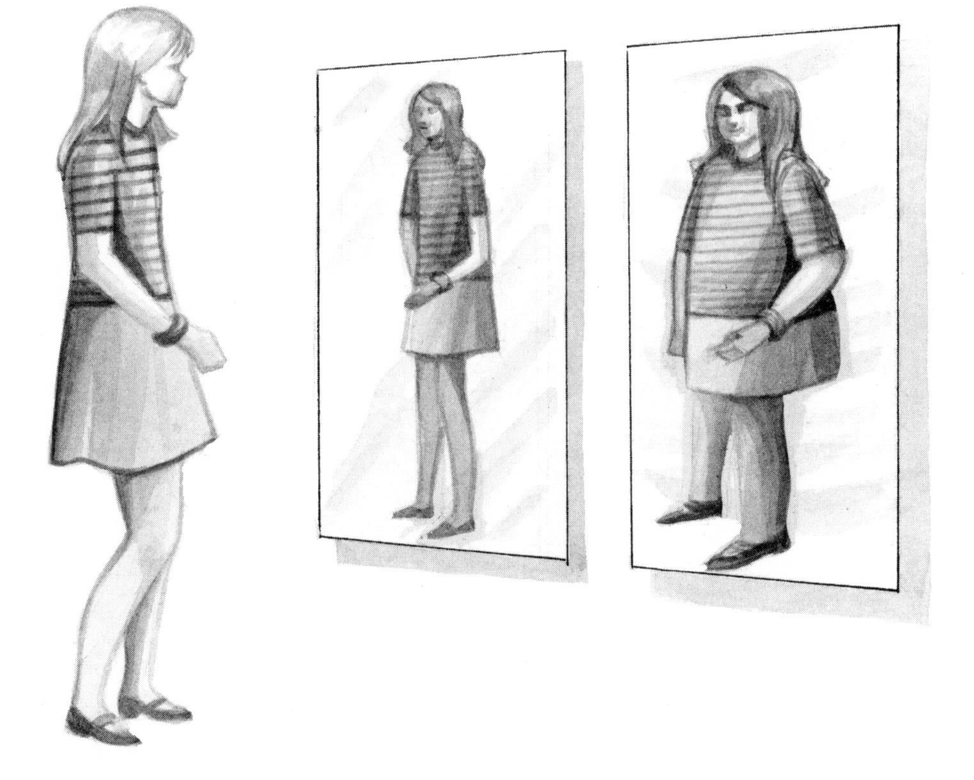

Light at Work

Light's tricks of refraction and reflection fool you if you don't know much about them. But if you study them and learn how they work, you can control them. By putting light to work for you through controlled refraction and reflection, you can do remarkable things that you couldn't do alone.

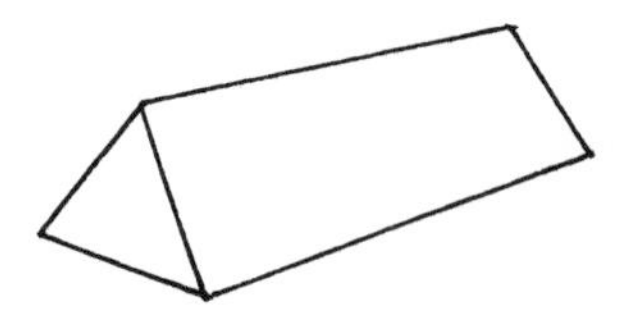

A Harness for Light

The simplest tool for harnessing light so that you can make it bend as you want, is a triangular glass prism. (The diagram shows what it looks like.) Let's see what happens when a thin beam of light is passed through the prism. Since the glass is denser than air, the light, when it enters the surface on the left, bends toward the normal. When it leaves through the surface on the other side, it bends away from the normal. In both cases the light has been brought nearer to the base of the prism. *The triangular prism has the effect of bending rays of light toward its base.*

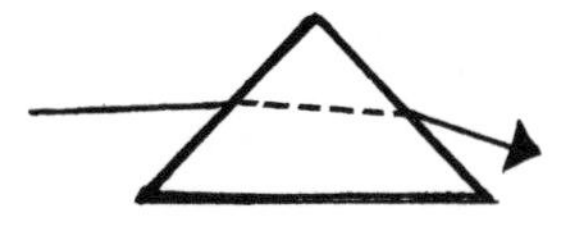

Archimedes' Death Ray

You have probably read about a death-ray machine in adventure stories. Archimedes, who lived over two thousand years ago, is actually supposed to have used one. When the Romans attacked his native city of Syracuse he set fire to their fleet by means of burning glasses that turned ordinary sunlight into an instrument of death and destruction. To see how this might be done, let's put two prisms together, base to base. Light passing through either prism is bent toward its base. Therefore light passing through the upper prism is bent down, while light passing through the lower prism is bent up. The combined effect of the two prisms is to make the rays of light come together or *converge* toward their common base in the middle. The effect is the same even if the sides of the prism are curved instead of flat, and the combination is made of one piece of glass instead of two. But what we have then is a *convex* lens—in other words, a *magnifying glass.*

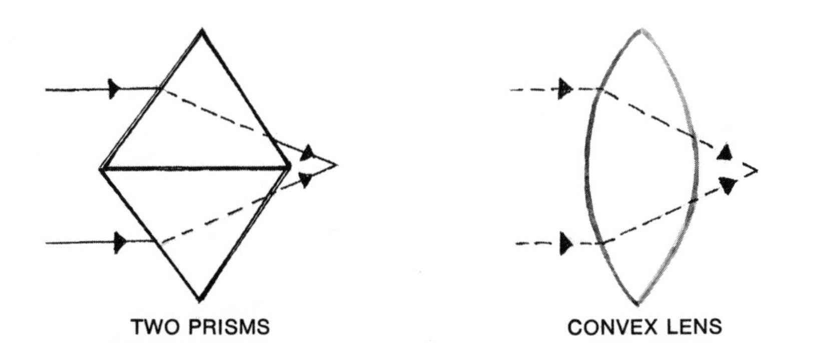

If a convex lens is held facing the sun, the rays of sunlight that pass through it will converge until they meet at a point on the other side. Since this concentrates heat rays as well as light into a small space, a piece of paper held at the point where they converge will catch fire. On a sunny summer day you can use a magnifying glass to light a match in this way.

In order to get enough heat to burn the Roman fleet, Archimedes would have had to catch a lot of sunlight with his burning-glasses. This would have meant making lenses of tremendous size. It is not likely that he was able to do this with the tools people had at that time, but it makes a good story anyhow.

MAGNIFYING GLASS

Making Things Look Larger

The point where the rays of light converge is called the *principal focus* of the lens. There is one on each side of the lens. The distance from the principal focus to the center of the lens is called the *focal length.*

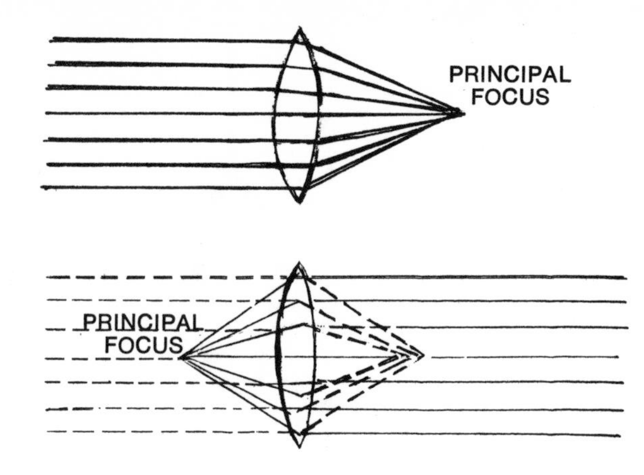

A single convex lens can be used to magnify small objects. Put an object in front of you at the level of your eyes. Now bring a lens between you and the object so that the object is between the lens and its principal focus. Because of the way the light is bent as it comes to you through the lens, light from the top of the object appears to come from a point farther away and higher, while light from the bottom appears to come from a point farther away and lower. As a result, the top and bottom of the object appear to be farther apart than they really are. And so the object looks larger.

When you look at an object through a window you see the object itself. But when you look at it through a lens you see an *image* of the object—an image that is larger than the object itself. The image that you see through a magnifying glass is called a *virtual image,* because it is made by light that *seems* to come from one place but actually comes from another. A single lens used in this way is called a *simple microscope.*

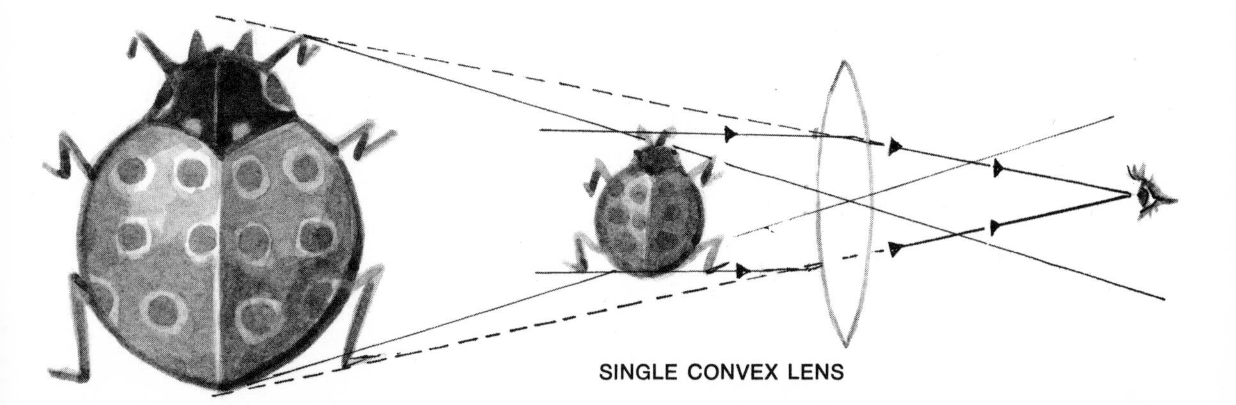

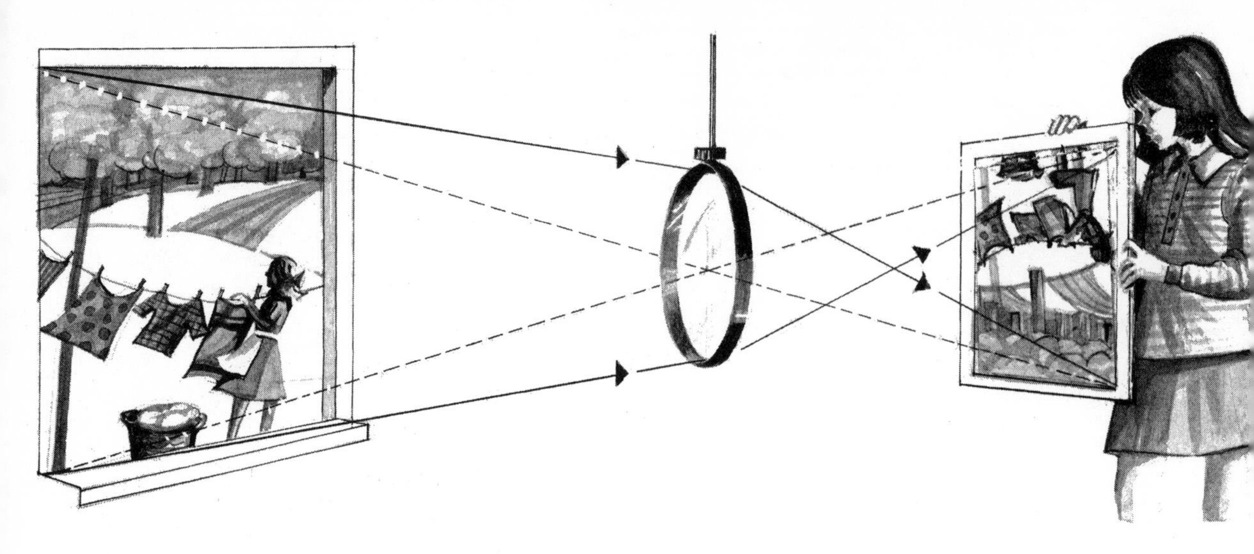

A Lens Makes Pictures

On a bright, sunny day, hold a magnifying glass close to a wall that is directly opposite a window. The light coming from the window and passing through the magnifying glass will form a blurred patch on the wall. Now slowly move the glass away from the wall. At one point the patch of light on the wall will grow sharp and distinct; it will be a picture of what you can see through the window. The picture will be upside down. A picture of this kind is called a *real image.* While a virtual image is an image from which the light only *seems* to come, a real image is formed at a place where the light really converges. If you allow a real image to form on a screen (or a wall), you see it as a picture on the screen that *really* sends light to your eye. The diagram shows you how this works.

To get this real image, we had the object (the window) at a distance from the lens greater than two focal lengths. The image was formed on the other side of the lens, on the wall, at a distance greater than one focal length but less than two. An image formed in this way is always smaller and upside down. To be able to see it, all you have to do is place a screen or a ground glass at the place where the image is formed.

The Camera

If you want to keep this picture permanently, you can put a piece of photographic film at the point where the image is formed.

The film is coated with a substance that is sensitive to light. When the film is placed in a chemical solution called a *developer,* dark spots appear in every part that was exposed to light. The result is called a *photographic negative.* It is called a *negative* because what you see is the opposite of the image. A light spot in the image caused the coating on the film to change and become black. But a dark spot in the image did not send out light to turn the coating black, and so it shows up white on the negative.

The process of printing the picture works in the same way. Photographic paper is also coated with a substance that is sensitive to light. When light comes through the white spots in the negative, it turns the paper black. Light cannot come through the black spots in the negative, and so the paper under these spots stays white. The printing gives you a *positive photograph,* a permanent copy of the real image formed by the lens. When you use a lens in this way, you have—a camera.

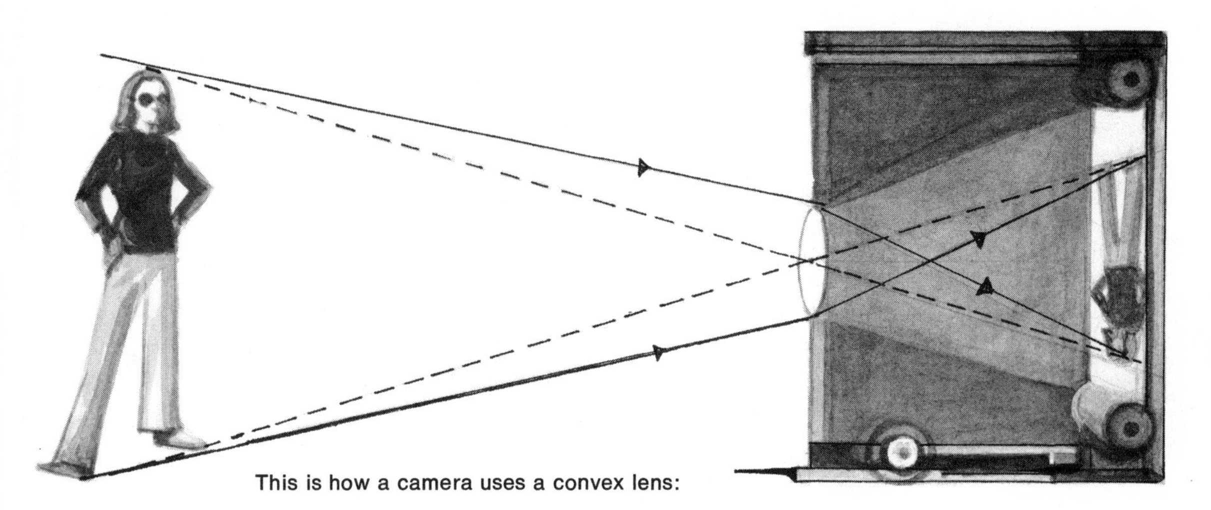

This is how a camera uses a convex lens:

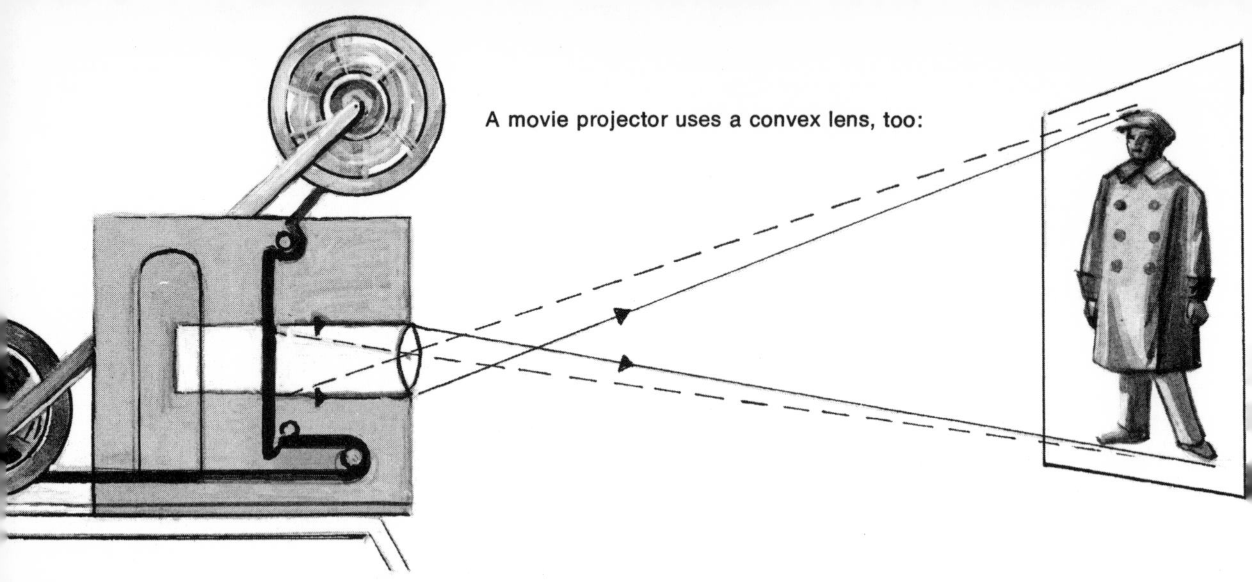

Big from Little

When the lens is used in a camera, a large object makes a small image. This process can be reversed, so that a small object will make a large image. To see how this works write a word on a piece of paper. Now hold the paper against a flashlight so that the light passes through the paper. By holding a magnifying glass between the flashlight and the wall, you can get an image of the word on the wall. If the distance from the flashlight to the magnifying glass is more than one focal length but less than two, and if the distance from the glass to the wall is more than two focal lengths, then the word will appear on the wall enlarged and upside down. If you hold the paper upside down, the image on the wall will be right side up. Lantern slides and movies are projected onto a screen by using a lens in this way.

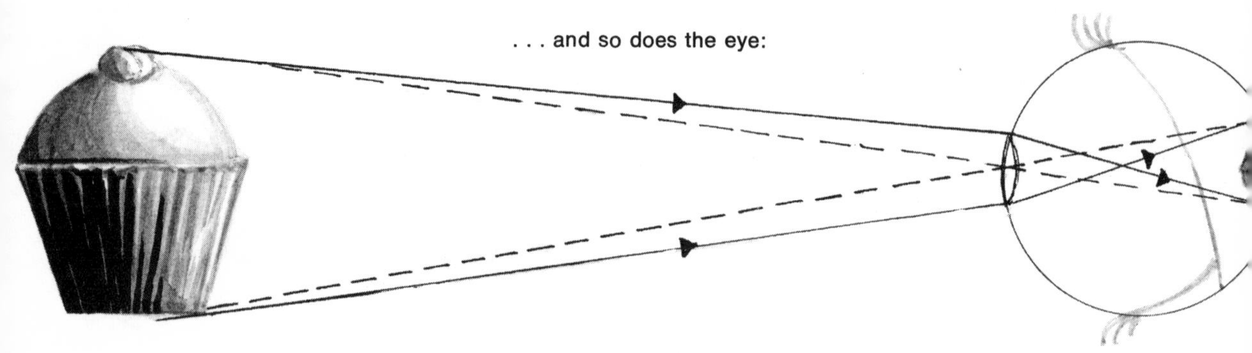

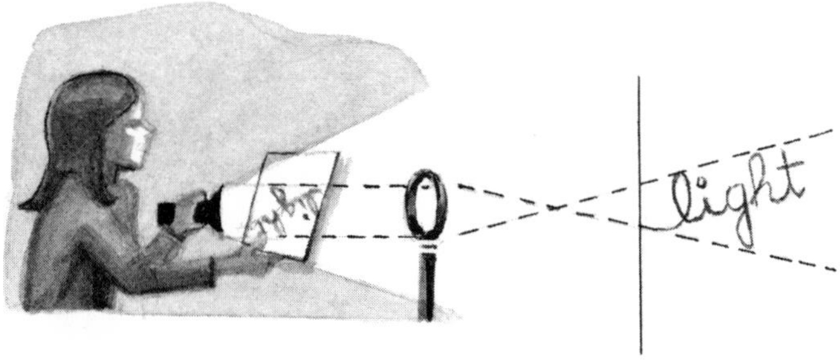

The Eye Is a Camera

Strictly speaking, the camera was not invented. It was copied, because it merely imitates the operation of the eye. Like a camera, the eye has a lens, and this forms an image on a sensitive screen at the back of the eye, called the retina. The optic nerve connects the retina with the brain, which interprets the image. And then you *see*.

But a lens, whether in a camera or in your eye, does not always form an image in exactly the same place. The farther away the object is in front of the lens, the farther away the image will be formed behind the lens. That's why cameras have focusing devices. They move the lens in or out to a position where the image will hit the film.

The eye focuses in a very different way. The lens does not move to and fro in front of the retina. It is always the same distance away.

The next three drawings show what would happen if the lens of the eye were always the same shape:

1. If the object is just the right distance away, the image would fall exactly on the retina.

2. If the object is closer to the eye, the image would be formed behind the retina, and the eye would see only a blur.

3. If the object is further away from the eye, the eye would also see a blur, because the image would be formed in front of the retina.

THESE PICTURES SHOW WHAT WOULD HAPPEN
IF THE LENS WERE ALWAYS THE SAME SHAPE:

The object is just the right distance away, so the image falls exactly on the retina.

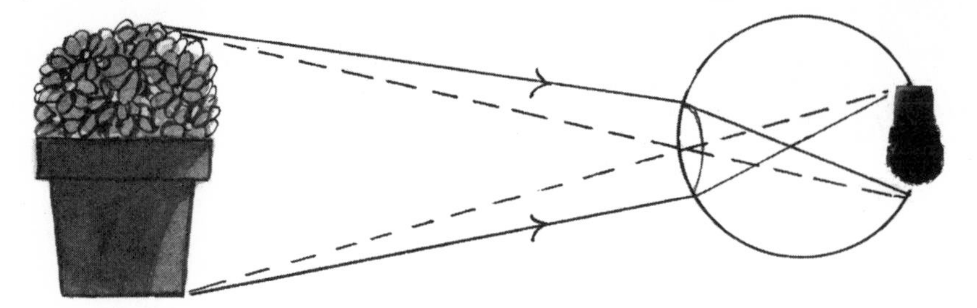

If the object is closer to the eye, the image would be formed behind the retina, and the eye would see only a blur.

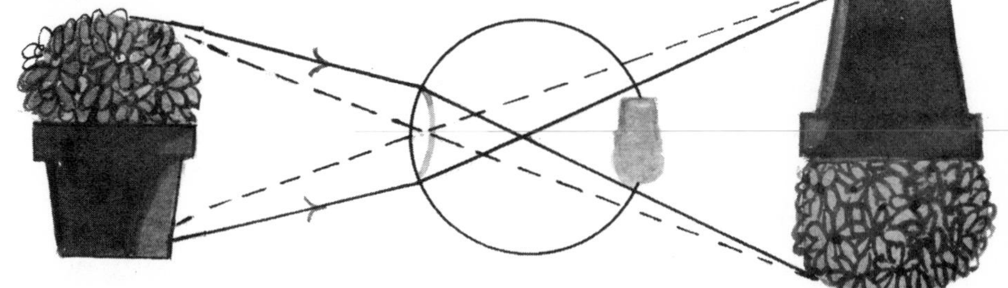

If the object is moved back, the eye would again see a blur, because the image would be formed in front of the retina.

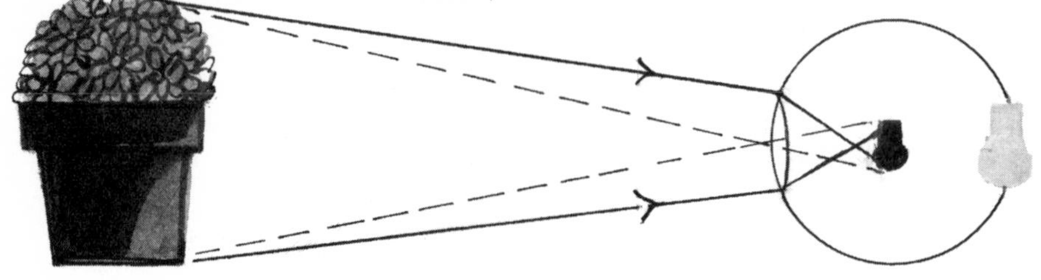

The action of the eye muscles prevents this. They change the shape of the lens, so that the image is always thrown exactly on the retina.

In many people's eyes, the muscles fail to adjust the shape of the lens properly. Such people have to make an artificial adjustment by using an extra glass lens in front of each eye. If a person is far-sighted, the lens of his eye is too thin, and the image is formed behind the retina. By using convex lenses in his eyeglasses, he can make the light converge more sharply, and form the image on the retina.

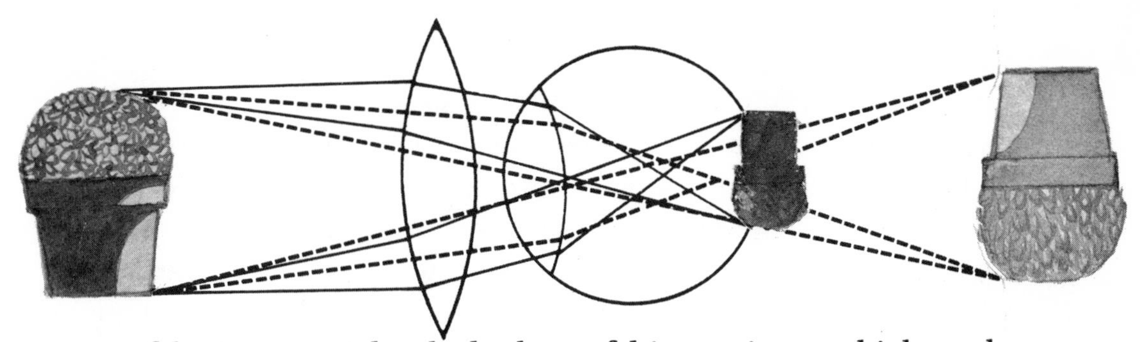

If he is near-sighted, the lens of his eye is too thick, and the image is formed in front of the retina. Then he must use a concave lens. This is like two prisms placed tip to tip. Since each prism bends light towards the base, a concave lens makes rays of light bend away from each other, or *diverge*. The concave lens makes the light converge less sharply, so that the image will fall *on* the retina instead of in front of it.

Seeing the Invisible

Now that we're equipped with eyeglasses and camera so that we can see better and can photograph what we see, it's time to look for new worlds to conquer. Let's prepare to invade the microscopic world, the world of things so small that you can't see them with the naked eye at all. To do this we have to use more than one lens.

One lens, called the *objective*, is placed inside a cylinder a little more than one focal length away from the *object* to be viewed. A large, real image is formed inside the cylinder of the instrument. A second lens, called the *eyepiece*, is placed less than one focal length away from the *image* inside the cylinder. This forms an even more enlarged virtual image of the already enlarged real image. And when you look through the eyepiece, that's what you see. A lens system like this is called a *compound microscope*. Biologists

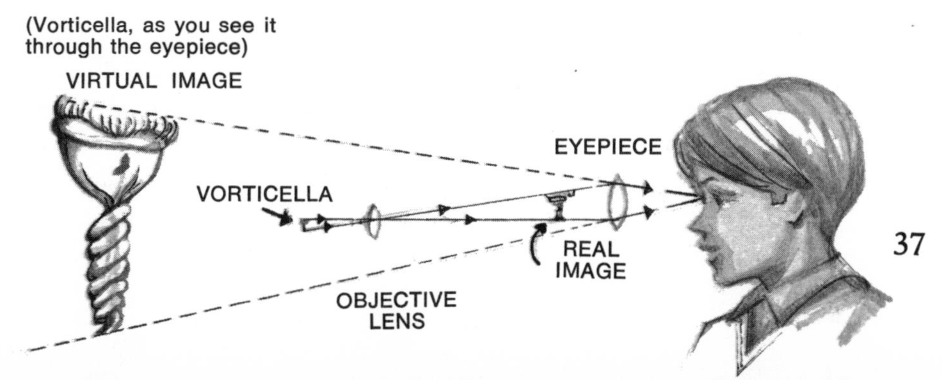

use it to examine the cell structure of living things, and to study the behavior of animals and plants too small for the eye to see. The microscope you use when you study biology will probably magnify things about 400 times. However, some microscopes can magnify as much as 5000 times. If *you* could be magnified that much, you could keep your feet on the ground and have your head above the clouds.

Leaping Through Space

There are other worlds to conquer far out in space: the moon and the planets, the sun and the stars. We can bring them close enough for study by using a lens system very much like the compound microscope—the telescope that can be used to scan the sky.

Magnifying glasses, cameras, projectors, eyeglasses, the compound microscope, and the refracting telescope are all based on light's habits of refraction. But another type of telescope takes advantage of the principle of reflection. Instead of an objective lens, it has a concave mirror. This makes the parallel rays of light that come in from a star converge at the focus. The 200-inch telescope on Mount Palomar in California—the largest telescope in the world—is a reflecting telescope of this type.

When light leaves a lamp, it travels out in all directions. But sometimes we want it to travel only in *one* direction. You can make light go where you want it by using a convex mirror in reverse. If the lamp is placed at the focus, the mirror will reflect all the rays straight out in one direction. Result—a single beam of light like that in an automobile headlight.

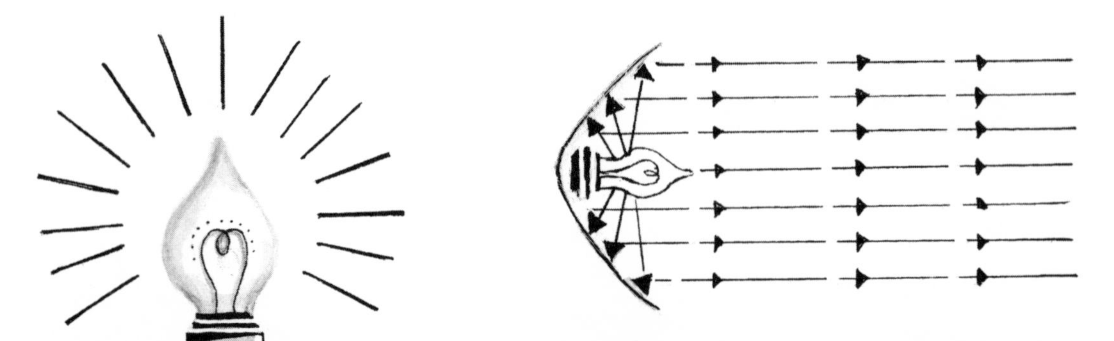

Going Backstage

The tricks of a magician on the stage are mysterious as long as you don't know how they are done. But if you go backstage and watch how the tricks are done, the mystery disappears. In fact, with the right tools and a little practice, you can do all the tricks yourself.

By learning light's tricks of reflection and refraction, we have broken down some of the mystery surrounding it. Thousands of years ago people thought light was a spirit or a god. Now we know it is only another part of nature. Its behavior can be studied, controlled, and put to work for us. The prisms, lenses, and mirrors we have just talked about are some of the tools with which this can be done.

Through their use, we have improved our eyesight. We have developed photography and moving pictures. With the telescope we have obtained a gold mine of information about the sun and the stars that helps us to understand more about the world we live in. And, with the help of the microscope, we have learned enough about the tiny cells that make up our bodies and the tinier germs that attack them to take great forward steps in the conquest of disease.

We have many more things to learn about light in the chapters that follow. For thousands of years, scientists have gone backstage to learn its tricks. We shall see, as we continue this story, how their knowledge of these tricks has made possible the invention of more and more tools. And with these tools man now uses nature to control nature.

Painting the World

A Dull World

Take a beautiful landscape, and remove all of the color. Wipe the blue out of the sky, the pink and gold out of the sunlit clouds. Take the green out of the leaves and grass. What is left would be a drab, lifeless gray, and most of the scene's beauty would be gone. A world without color would be a mighty dull place to live in!

What is responsible for the many colors of the world we live in? What puts the red in the rose, the blue in the sea?

Take a brightly colored picture into a room whose only source of light is a lamp. Now switch off the lamp and look at the picture. The colors are gone! When the light went, out the colors went with them. Light must be responsible for the colors, since we see them only when it is here.

Finding the Colors

How can white light, which we usually think of as uncolored, be responsible for the colors we see around us? Where are the colors hidden? The great English scientist, Isaac Newton, answered this question nearly three hundred years ago when he discovered that white light is a mixture of colored light and contains all the colors within itself. He showed this by passing a thin beam of light through a triangular prism. While white light entered the prism, it was colored light that left it. As we saw before, the prism bends the light toward the base. However, it doesn't bend all colors equally. So the colors bent most come out closest to the base, while the colors bent least come out farthest from the base. As a result, while the colors were united when they entered the prism, they were spread out when they left it, and could be seen separately. The colors that appear are, from top to bottom, red, orange, yellow, green, blue, indigo, violet. This spread-out sequence of colors is called a *spectrum*.

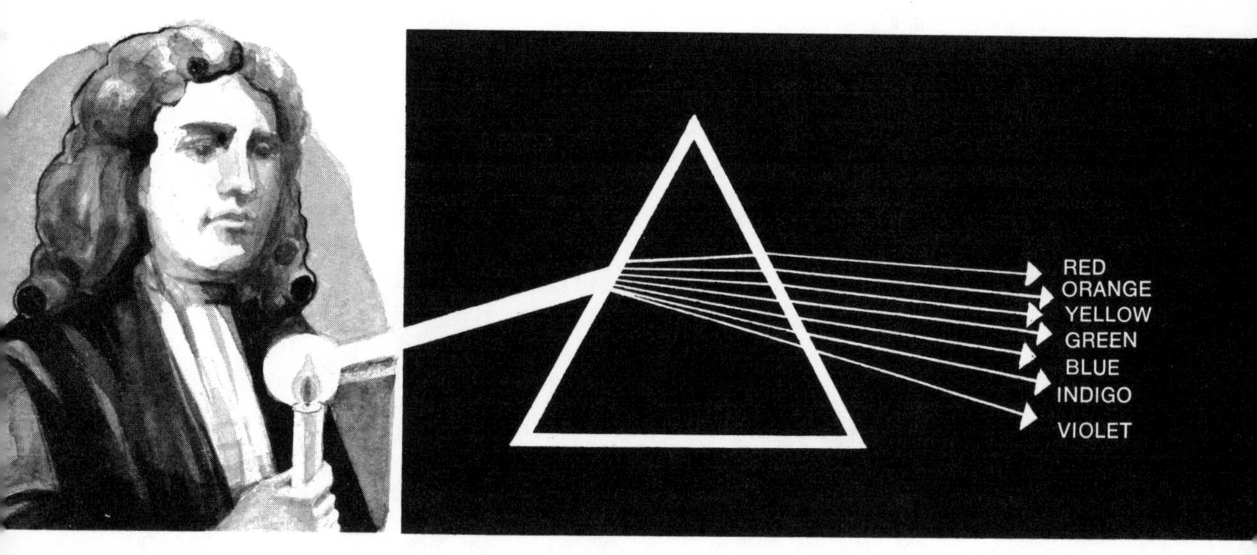

How, then, does white light make things look colored? All the colors are already present in the white light. Turn white light on a red rose. Because of the particular chemicals of which the rose petals are made, they absorb some of the light and reflect the rest. Only the reflected light reaches your eye. Since the petals have absorbed almost all of the light except the red, which is reflected, they look red. Now look at the leaves. The same thing happens here, only this time it is the green light which is reflected. Everything gets its color in this way. When light is turned on an object, the object reflects and sends to your eye only some of the colors present in the light, and absorbs the rest. *The color of an object is the color of the light it sends to your eye.*

Changing Colors

Because of this fact, you can change the color of an object merely by putting it in different light. Here's the way to do it. Get a beam of green light by passing ordinary sunlight

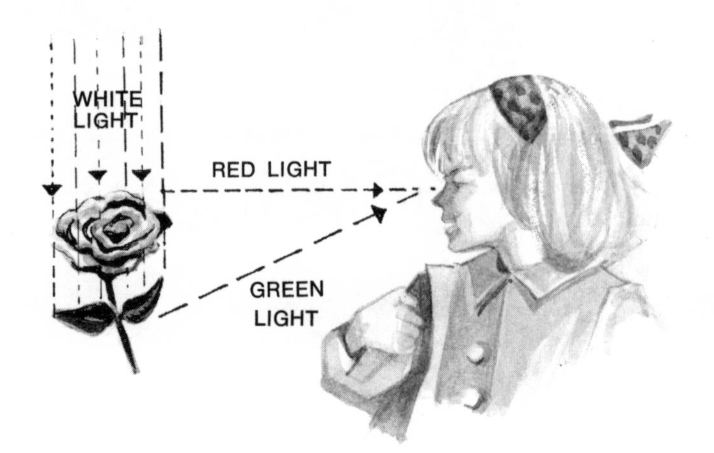

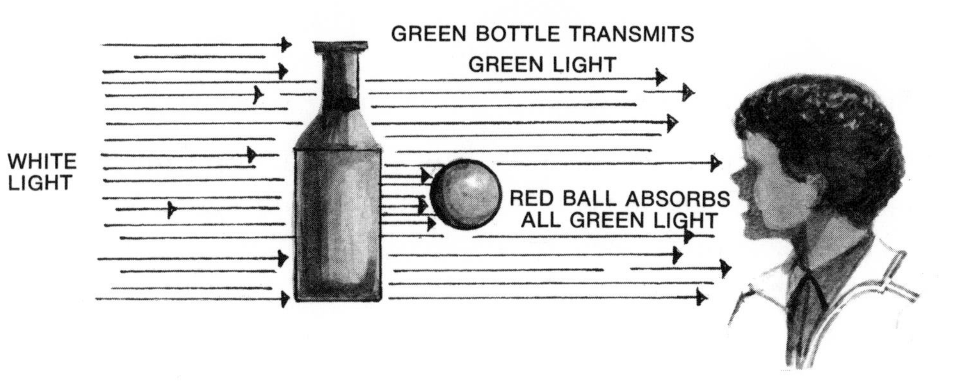

through a green soda water bottle. Now hold a red object—a ball for instance—in the green light, and keep all other light out. The ball is no longer red! It is black instead! Why? Because there is no red in green light. Therefore, since the ball didn't receive any red light, it couldn't send it to your eye. Since a red object absorbs all colors except red, it absorbed all the green light. Therefore it reflected no light at all. An object that reflects no light at all is black. Because the color of an object depends on the kind of light that is turned on it, when you buy clothes be sure to look at the colors in sunlight. They won't be the same by the incandescent light of the clothing store, because incandescent light doesn't have as much blue as sunlight does.

The Spectrum on the Bathroom Wall

Every day I find a spectrum on my bathroom wall. It has all the colors ranging from red to violet. It comes and goes by itself in a very simple way. The mirror on my medicine chest has a beveled edge. This edge is like a triangular prism. When the sunlight streaming in through the window is reflected onto the wall by the beveled edge, it is separated into the colors of the spectrum.

The same separation of sunlight into its colors is sometimes carried out by glass doorknobs or by glass beads hanging from chandeliers. Because of their angular shapes, they, too, act as prisms.

The Spectrum on the Pavement

Sometimes oil drips out of a car and forms a thin film on the pavement. If you have seen one of these oil spots, you must have been impressed by its brilliant colors and the way the colors shifted and changed as you walked by. The separation of the colors here is the result of the fact that the light is reflected from two surfaces that are very close to each other—the top and bottom of the oil. Because of *interference,* which you will find out about in the next chapter, some of the colors in the white light are cancelled out. The ones that are left are those you see.

Get a bubble pipe or wand and make some soap bubbles. Notice the colors in the bubbles. They look brilliantly colored for the same reason that the oil film does. The bubble's thin film of soapy water reflects light from both its inner and outer surfaces. Because the two surfaces are so close together, interference cancels out some of the colors. You see the ones that are not cancelled out.

The Rainbow

Long before Isaac Newton used a prism to make a spectrum, people had seen one in the sky—the rainbow. When droplets of rain water reflect the sunlight, they separate its colors. Of course, a rainbow appears only if the sun is out while it rains. To see the rainbow, be sure to stand with your back to the sun.

According to the story of Noah in the Bible, the rainbow was God's sign of promise that no flood would ever come again to destroy all living things.

Today we know that the rainbow is a natural occurrence, but it is easy to see how this belief started. Imagine the people thousands of years ago overwhelmed by a tropical rain lasting for days and days. To them it certainly must have looked as though the heavens had opened up. Remembering the legends they had heard from their fathers about a flood that destroyed all living things, they were naturally afraid. Anxiously they scanned the sky for any sign that the storm would soon come to an end. After many such stormy experiences, they found a sign: if the storm died out when the sun was low in the sky, as the first rays of sunlight broke through the clouds, they saw the rainbow arching across the heavens. They soon learned that the rainbow was a sure sign that the rain was over. What *was* this beautiful sign in the heavens that promised them safety from the terrors of the storm? They could see it, but they could not touch it. They could walk toward it, but they could never reach it. They did not know that they were merely seeing the rays of the sun reflected and broken up by droplets of water in the air. They knew only that the rainbow was connected with the end of the storm. But they did not know how, or why. Since they saw it in the heavens, the mysterious home of the sun, the moon and the stars, the wind, the lightning, and the storm itself, they believed it was somehow divine. Many of the religious beliefs of ancient man began in this way, when men did not yet know enough about the world around them to break down the mystery surrounding great natural occurrences. Through myth and legend, they filled in with fantasy the gaps in their knowledge.

What is Light?

A Portrait of Light

After scientists had begun to study the way light acts, they worked out two different ideas about the nature of light. At first these ideas did not agree. But as scientists have studied light still further, they have come to realize that both are right. One portrait of light is given by the theory, advanced by Newton, that light consists of a stream of particles or corpuscles traveling in straight lines or rays. By means of this theory it is possible to explain many things, including the laws of mirrors and lenses, and the formation of shadows. The other view of light, advanced by the Dutch scientist, Christian Huyghens, at about the same time, is that light is a train of waves traveling through space. This theory also explains the laws of mirrors and lenses very well, and even the formation of shadows. Nevertheless, Newton's theory was favored for a long time and Huyghens' was almost forgotten. Then, in 1801, an English scientist named Thomas Young did an experiment that could not be explained at all by Newton's corpuscular theory!

Young's experiment had a remarkable result. He found that by adding two quantities of light you don't always get more light. Sometimes you get darkness. In his experiment he allowed light of a single color to pass through a small hole in one screen and fall on another screen in front of it. The result was a patch of light on the second screen. When he used two holes close together in the first screen, two overlapping patches of light were formed on the second screen. But the region where they overlapped, instead of being brighter because of the addition of two quantities of light, was crossed by dark lines. The dark lines indicated places where the streams of light from the two holes, instead of reinforcing each other, interfered with each other and cancelled each other out. This *interference* of light can be explained very well by the wave theory.

Water Waves

It helps us to understand light waves if we first examine another kind of wave that we can actually see. Drop a stone into a pond. The water is disturbed, but the disturbance is not limited to the place where the stone struck the water. Instead, it travels away from that point in a circular wave, which grows wider and wider as it moves away from the source of the disturbance. Float a ball in a pool. Now take a stick and push the ball up and down rhythmically. You will see a whole train of circular waves, one following the other, traveling out from the same point.

Something is obviously sweeping across the surface of the water. Is it the water itself that is moving away from the center of the disturbance? Here's a way you can find out. Put a cork on the surface of the water at a point where the oncoming waves will hit it. Do the waves sweep the cork away? No, they do not. As the waves pass, *the cork stays in the same place, bobbing up and down.* This shows that the only motion of the water is this bobbing up and down, or *vibration.* The water does not travel with the wave. What does travel is the up-and-down *motion,* which each particle of water passes on to its neighbors. Since motion is a form of energy, the wave transfers energy from one part of the water to another.

Ups and Downs, High and Low

The diagram shows what the surface of the water looks like, at a given moment, along a line drawn from the center of the disturbance. The high points of the waves are called crests; the low points are called troughs. When a crest passes the cork, it will move up; when a trough passes it, the cork will move down. The distance between two neighboring crests is called the *wave length.* The number of crests that pass the cork in one second is called the *frequency.* Since the speed with which the wave travels is fixed, it travels a definite distance in one second. The number of crests that pass the cork in one second will be the number of waves needed to fill in that distance. The shorter the waves are, the more of them there will be in that distance. Therefore, waves of short wave length have a high frequency, and waves of long wave length have a low frequency.

You started the train of waves in the water by pushing a ball up and down. If you push gently, the waves are not very high. The harder you push, the higher the waves. When you push harder, you are giving the particles of

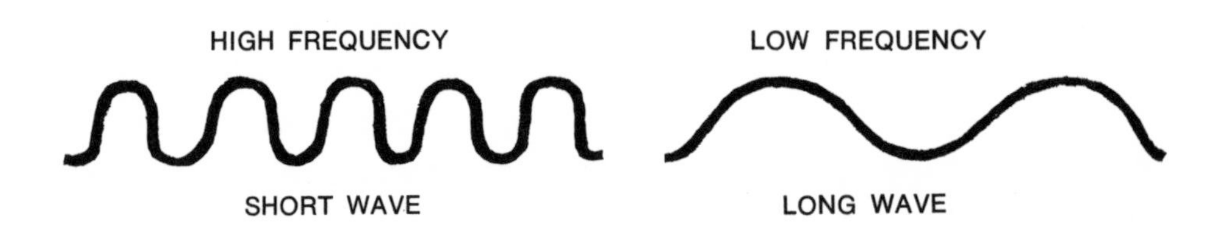

water more energy of motion. The height of the waves, known as the *amplitude,* therefore shows the amount of energy that is being transferred from one particle of water to another.

When Waves Meet

Now try putting two balls not very far apart in the pool of water, and push them both up and down with the same rhythm. Each bobbing ball sets up a system of circular waves that travel across the surface of the water. The two wave systems cross each other and therefore will act on some particles of water at the same time. Where a crest of one system comes together with a crest of the other system, the water gets two upward pushes combined and moves up higher. Where a trough comes together with a trough, the water gets two downward pushes combined and moves down even lower. But something quite different happens when a crest comes together with a trough. The crest is pushing the water up while the trough is pushing the water down. *The two pushes cancel each other, and the water at that point doesn't move at all.* The result, as you can see in the picture, is a series of lines where the water is smooth and undisturbed. These are like the interference lines which Young discovered in his experiment with light.

The Secret of Colored Light

The water waves we examined were circles. Light waves traveling out from a glowing point are not limited to any surface, but go out in all directions and are therefore spherical in shape. Just as in the case of the water wave, there is a vibration which is being transferred through space. Every simple case of transfer of light energy has its wave length, frequency, and amplitude. If Young's experiment is done with two parallel slits instead of two holes, the interference of the light will make parallel dark lines where crests and troughs cancel each other. Knowing the distance between the slits, the distance between neighboring dark lines, and the distance from the slits to the screen on which the light falls, it is possible to calculate the wave length of the light. Since we know the speed of light, we can figure out the frequency for each wave length.

We can now explain how one color is different from another. Lights of different color are waves of different wave lengths. When we form a spectrum from white light, we are separating the different wave lengths mixed in the white light. At the same time, we are arranging these wave lengths in order of size, from violet, which is the shortest, to red, which is the longest. All these wave lengths are very small. Violet light waves are so small, that there are over 60,000 to an inch. Red light waves are twice as long, and so there are about 30,000 to an inch. Because the speed of light is so great (186,000 miles per second), each color represents a vibration of extremely high frequency. In green light, for example, 600 *million million* waves will pass any spot in one second!

A Double Exposure

After the wave theory of light was firmly established, a new discovery was made that brought Newton's corpuscular theory back to life. It was found, as a result of discoveries by the German physicists, Max Planck and Albert Einstein, that light is always issued or absorbed in indivisible little bundles of energy. It's as though the light source were acting like a machine gun, firing out little bullets of light one after the other. These have been called *photons*. Therefore, while light is still to be considered a wave motion, it may also be thought of as a stream of photons. We now have a portrait of light, but it looks like a double exposure: two pictures on the same plate. It is a wave and a stream of particles at the same time!

Interference Helps

We have just become familiar with a new trick light can play, the trick of canceling itself out to form dark interference bands. Now that we know the secret of the trick, we can take advantage of it by using a very useful instrument, the grating. If a large number of parallel lines are scratched close together on a metal mirror (as many as 15,000 to an inch), the scratches will have the same effect as the holes or slits in Young's experiment. The light reflected by the mirror will form interference bands. Here, however, the bands of light will be narrow, and the dark bands separating them will be wide. If the light used is white, which is a mixture of all colors, each color will be reflected in a slightly different direction, so that the bands of colored light will appear side by side. Close to each violet band will be a blue band, then green, yellow, orange and red, in the same order in which they appear in a rainbow. The grating, like the prism, therefore separates the colors in mixed light into a spectrum. But it also has this special advantage: By means of the grating you can measure the wave length of each of the colors.

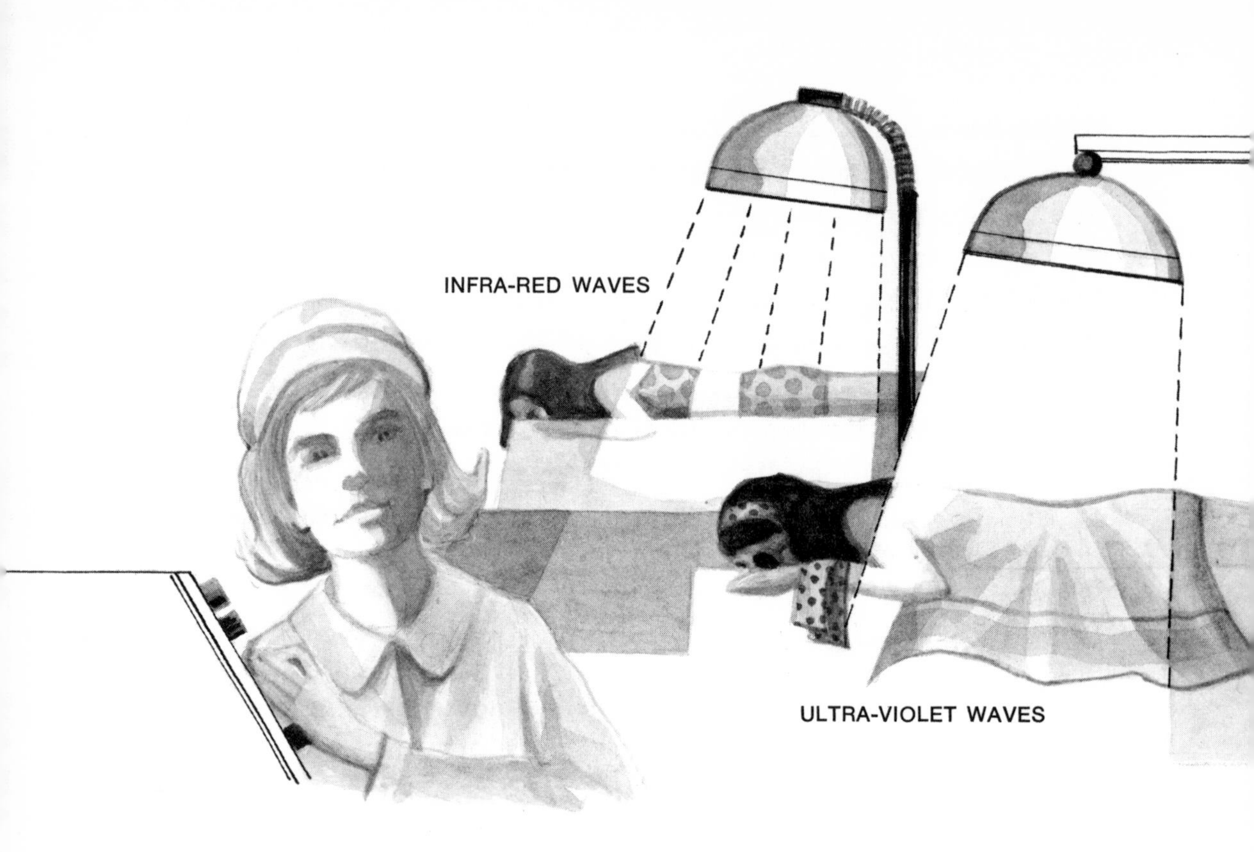

Invisible Light

Light's Family

We think of light as something we can see. But is that all light is? Let's look a little further. We'll find that some things we didn't think of as light, at first, turn out to be closely related to it.

Pass some sunlight through a prism to get the spectrum. What wonderfully gay colors—from red to violet. Each wave length of light appears to us as a color we can see. But we can also detect its presence in another way. Hold a sensitive thermometer in the spectrum. The mercury rises, which shows that it is receiving heat. The light is heating the body on which it falls. Now move the thermometer into the dark region just beyond the red. You can't see any light there, so you would expect the thermometer to fall again. Instead, *it rises even higher*. This shows the presence of a part of the spectrum that *cannot be seen*—a part that was hidden in the sunlight all the time. Because it is beyond the red, it is called *infrared* light. Its wave length is longer, and its frequency is lower than that of red light. Because infrared rays can be detected by their heating effect, they are sometimes referred to as *heat waves*. Doctors use infrared lamps to provide heat in certain medical treatments.

Since we found something in the spectrum beyond the red, let's try our luck beyond the violet. Here we can find more invisible light by using a photographic plate. Since this hidden light is beyond the violet, it is called *ultraviolet* light. Its wave length is shorter and its frequency is higher than that of violet light. Ultraviolet light is responsible for sunburn in the summertime.

We know now that visible light is only one member of a larger family, the family of *energy radiation*. Each member of this family is a wave that travels through space at the same speed light does, and each has its own wave length and frequency.

But what causes these waves anyway? Experiments with electricity and magnetism gave the answer to this question.

Two New Clues

There are two kinds of electric charges, called *positive* and *negative*. If two charges are of the same kind, each *pushes* against the other. If they were free to move, they would separate. If two charges are of opposite kinds, each *pulls* on the other. If they were free to move, they would move toward each other. You can see these effects for yourself

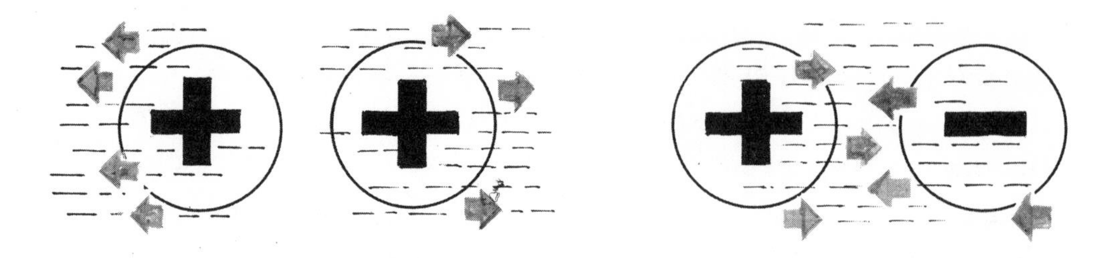

when you comb your hair with a hard rubber comb on a day when the air is very dry. As a result of the rubbing of the comb against your hair, both the comb and your hair become electrically charged. If you then hold the comb near your hair, strands of hair will move toward the comb. This is because the hair and the comb have opposite charges. Meanwhile, you will notice that individual hairs stand out from your head in all directions, as if they were trying to get as far away from each other as possible. This is because all the hairs have the same kind of charge. When a body has an electric charge on it, we say that it is surrounded by an *electrical field.*

Magnets also exert pushes and pulls on each other. Each magnet has two ends called *poles.* One is called north, and the other south. If you hold two horseshoe magnets close to each other, so that the north pole on one is next to the south pole on the other, they exert a strong pull toward

each other. Now, if you turn one of the magnets over, the north pole on one will be next to the north pole on the other, and the magnets will push each other away. If you try to force them together, the space between them will feel as bouncy as rubber, and the magnets will simply jump apart. When a piece of metal is magnetized, we say it is surrounded by a *magnetic field.*

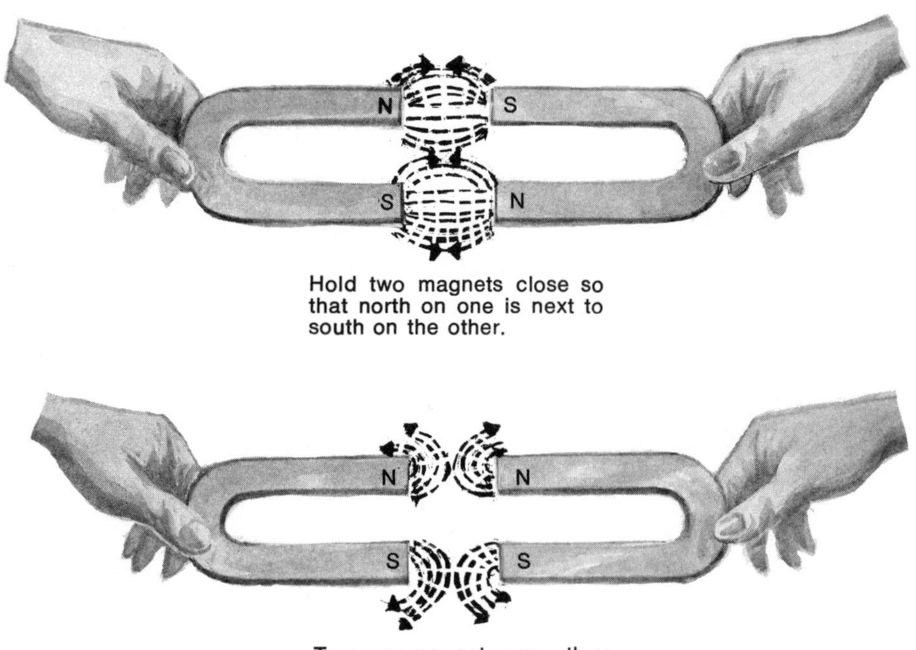

Hold two magnets close so that north on one is next to south on the other.

Turn one magnet over — they will push each other away.

That these two fields—the electrical and the magnetic—are closely related was established by the work of two physicists, Hans Christian Oersted, a Dane, and Michael Faraday, an Englishman, more than a hundred years ago. Oersted showed that a moving electric charge or electric current in a wire is surrounded by a magnetic field. Faraday showed that a moving magnetic field will cause an electric current to flow in a wire. That the two fields are related to light was shown by another Englishman, James Clerk Maxwell. A current that moves back and forth rapidly in a wire causes rapid changes in the surrounding electric and magnetic fields. Maxwell showed that these changes move out into space in the form of a wave and travel with the speed of light. These waves are called *electromagnetic waves*. They are, in fact, the same as light waves, except that they have a longer wave length. The light we can see consists of electromagnetic waves—but only of the ones to which the retina of our eye is sensitive.

Light That Talks

Following Maxwell's studies, Heinrich Hertz, a German scientist, produced some electromagnetic waves of a wave length much longer than infrared. These are now known as *radio waves,* and they are the foundation of radio broadcasting. As everybody knows, radio waves carry messages that our radio receivers can convert into human voices.

You can't see radio waves, but they let us know they are there by talking to us!

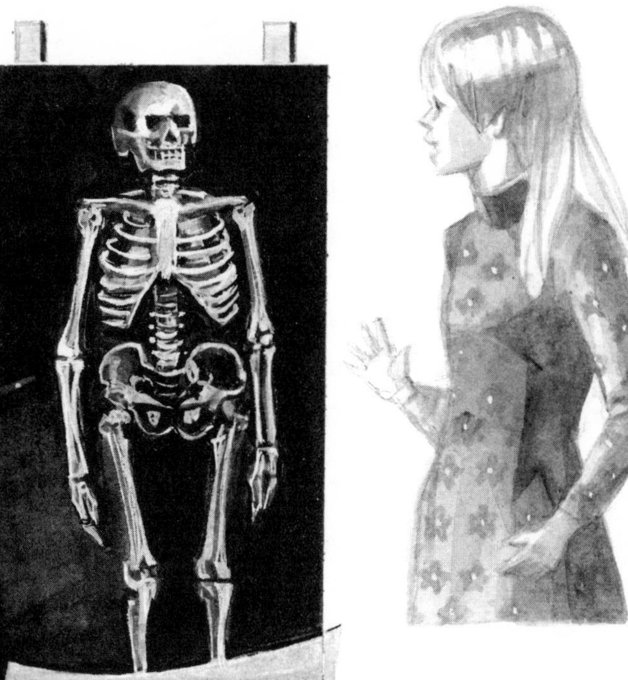

Hard Light

When you take a photograph, the picture shows your skin, but not your bones. This is so because the light used to take the picture cannot break through your flesh to reach the bones. However, it is possible to take a picture of your bones, too. All you have to do is use *X-rays* instead of light. X-rays, first discovered by Wilhelm Roentgen in 1895, have the power to crash through solids that can stop ordinary light. X-rays that can penetrate very far are called *hard* X-rays. They are merely electromagnetic waves of very short wave length, shorter than ultraviolet. Because the wave length is so short, the frequency is very high. A higher frequency means greater energy and greater penetrating power.

The hardest rays of all are gamma rays that result when the earth's atmosphere is bombarded by fast moving charged particles called cosmic rays crashing in from outer space. Gamma rays are also spontaneously released by radium.

A Family Portrait

Born of electricity and magnetism which are married in a vibrating electrical current, all forms of light are electromagnetic radiations or waves. If we line them up in order of wave length, we get an enlarged spectrum of which Newton's spectrum is only a part. Starting with the shortest waves, we find them in this order: gamma rays, X-rays, ultraviolet rays, visible light ranging from violet to red, infrared rays, and radio waves.

By studying their characteristics we have learned how to use each of them. Gamma rays, because of their high energy, are used by doctors to kill cancer cells. X-rays are used by doctors for taking pictures of the inside of your body. Ultraviolet light, obtained from sun lamps, can be used for helping your body manufacture the vitamin D it needs. Infrared rays, besides being used for heat treatments, are also useful for taking photographs through haze and fog. Radio waves carry radio and television broadcasts from the station to receivers in our homes and elsewhere. And of course, you remember the many uses of *visible* light already described.

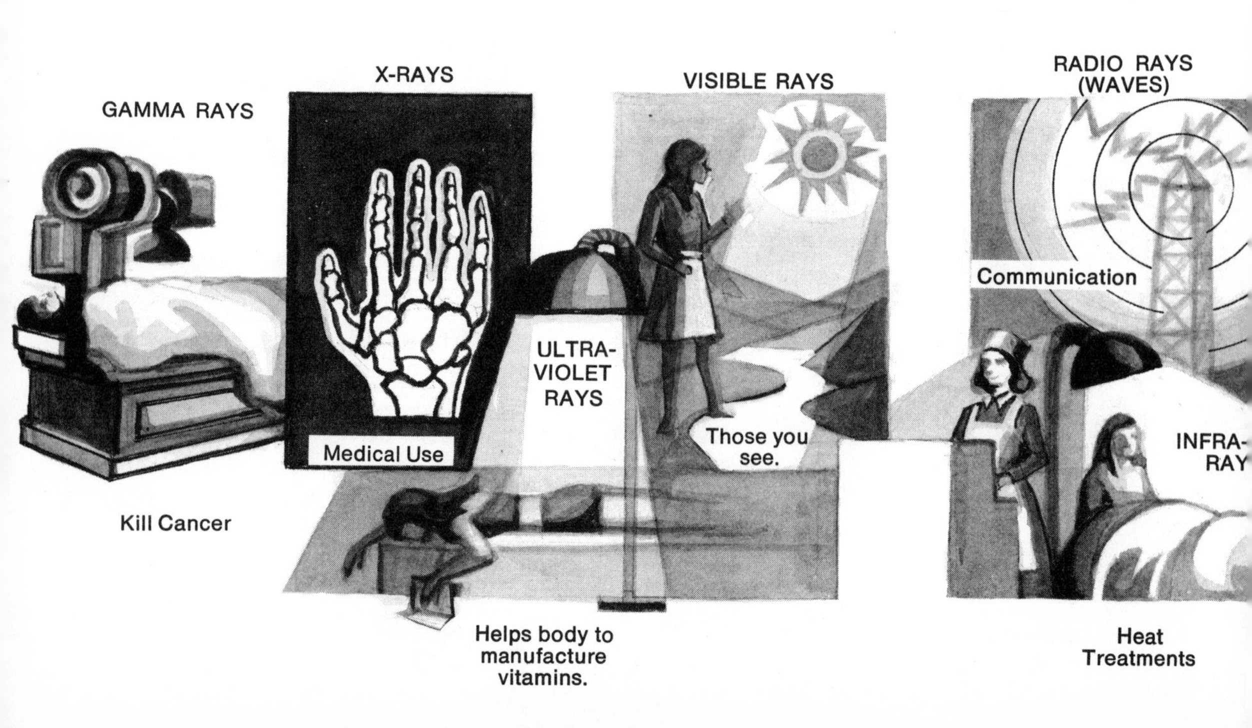

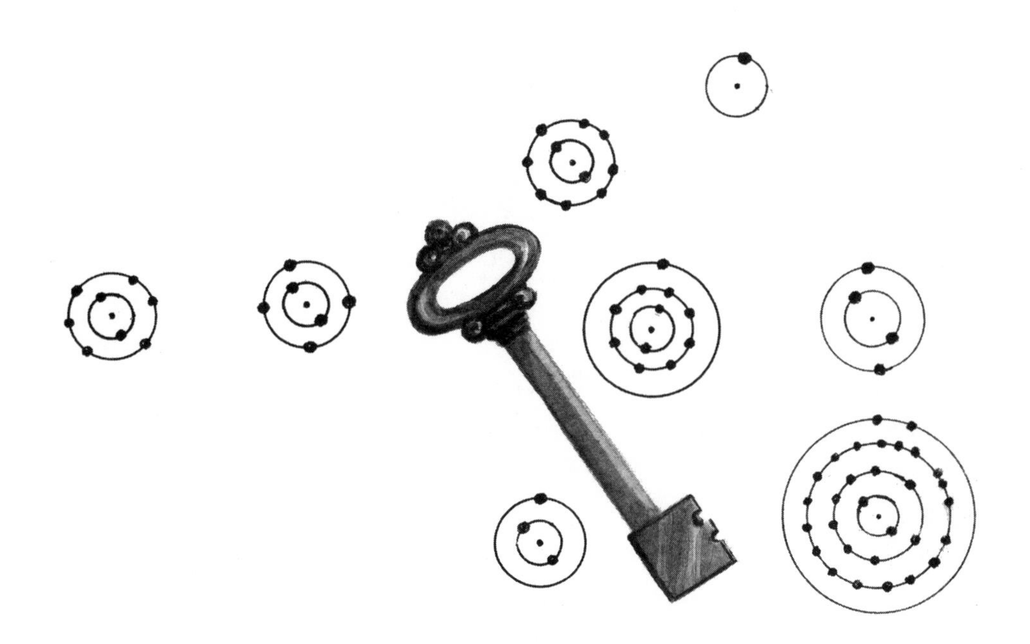

Unlocking the Secrets of the Atom

We are now ready to start out on one of the most exciting adventures of modern times, exploring the mysteries of atomic structure. The road we take on our trip will be lit up by a powerful beacon, our knowledge of light.

Nature's Building Blocks

What are atoms?

Over two thousand years ago, about 400 B.C., the Greek philosopher Democritus tried to figure out what the world is made of and how it came to be the way it is. He came to the conclusion that all things are made up of tiny particles, too small to be seen. There are many kinds, he thought, and they are always moving about, sometimes combining, and sometimes separating again.

Democritus deserves tremendous credit for giving us this theory. In the past people have believed in many ideas which new knowledge and experience later proved false. But all the discoveries of science in over two thousand years of work and study show that Democritus was right. Investigation by chemists has shown that every chemical compound, such as salt or water, is made up of many tiny particles called *molecules.* In solids and liquids they are packed closely together. In gases they are spread out thin, with big spaces separating the molecules from each other. Each molecule in a *compound* is the same as all the other molecules in the same compound, but it is different from the molecules in other compounds. Since there are thousands of different compounds, there are thousands of different kinds of molecules, ranging from simple ones, like the molecules of salt or water, to very complicated ones found only in living things.

Further study showed that the molecules themselves are made up of still smaller particles known as *atoms.* Although there are thousands of different molecules, there are only about 100 different kinds of atoms. These different atoms, known as the *chemical elements,* are the building blocks out of which all material things are made.

Outside Looking In

If you want to examine a big building, all you have to do, sometimes, is open the door and walk in. Then you can see it from the inside. We can't do that with the atom, because it is so small. Whatever we learn about the atom we must discover by looking at it from the outside.

Maybe some light will help us. Let's turn a beam of light on the atom so we can see it. That doesn't help us much, for two reasons. First, an atom is so tiny that even through the most powerful microscope, it is still too small to be seen. Second, the light that you shine on an atom would give it such a kick that it wouldn't stand still long enough to be seen.

Then how can we use light to see into the inside of the atom? To get the answer to that question we must first learn one thing more about light itself: Where does light come from anyway?

Who Broadcasts Light?

We know the answer for the long electromagnetic waves of radio. Radio waves are sent out by a radio transmitter, which is a rapidly vibrating electric current. Is there a transmitter that sends out visible light waves? Well, let's see where the light we use generally comes from. Daylight comes from the sun, which is a mass of hot, glowing gas. Lamplight usually comes from a hot, glowing wire. Apparently, then, solids and gases can glow, or send out light. Since even tiny quantities of a solid or a gas can be made to glow, the light must come from the smallest particles of which these materials are made. *The transmitters that send out light must be vibrating molecules or atoms.*

This fact tells us how to use light to unlock the secrets of the atom. Instead of shining light on the atom from the outside, we must capture and study the light that comes from *inside* the atom. This should give us clues to the way the atoms vibrate, and what they are made of.

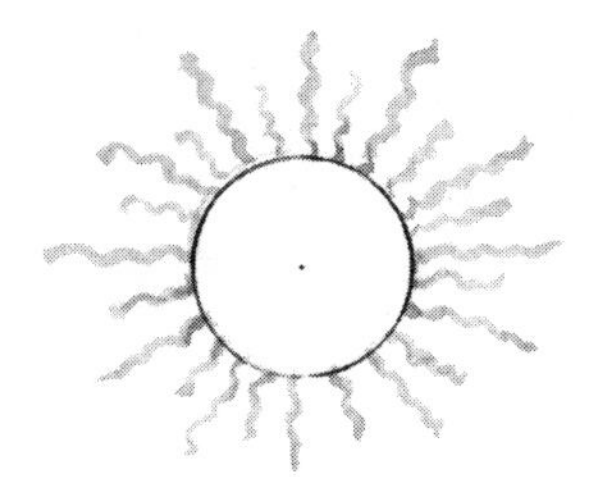

Fingerprinting the Elements

In a solid or a liquid, the atoms and molecules are so close together that they influence each other quite a bit. Therefore their vibrations are very complicated. To give each atom of an element a chance to vibrate in its own way, undisturbed by its neighbors, we must arrange to have the atoms far apart from each other. This can be done by using the element in the form of a gas, in which the atoms are separated from each other by great distances compared to their own size.

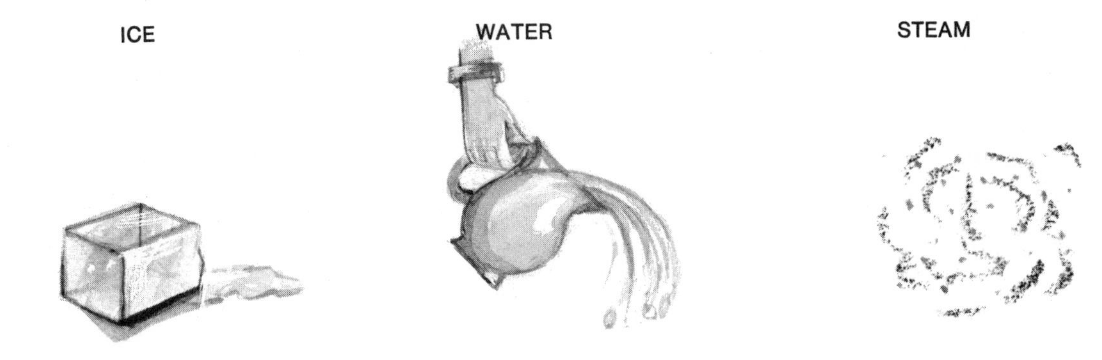

ATOMS AND MOLECULES ARE VERY CLOSE TOGETHER IN SOLIDS AND LIQUIDS, BUT FAR APART IN GASES.

An element in the form of a gas can be made to glow either by heating it or by passing an electric current through it. This glow is a mixture of colors, as we found out before. If the light of this glow is passed through a spectroscope, the colors can be separated, and their frequencies can be measured. The spectrum of an element in gaseous form is a series of disconnected lines, called a *brightline spectrum.* The lines you get from one element are different from the lines you get from any other element. This remarkable fact gives us a powerful method for identifying the elements. Just as you can identify a person by his fingerprints, you can identify an element by the lines in its spectrum.

Do you want to see this glow of atoms yourself? You don't need a spectroscope. You can do this simple experiment. Sprinkle some table salt over a gas flame. The flame, normally blue, will turn yellow. The yellow glow comes from the sodium atoms, some of which are separated from the salt by the flame. You see another example of glowing atoms in the neon lights used in many storefronts.

The Key to the Secrets of the Atom

The spectrum of an element is more than just another way of identifying it. Since it comes from inside the atom, it can help us discover the secret of what atoms are like. Every little line in the spectrum of an element is a message from the atom. If we only know how to read this message, we can solve the mystery of the structure of the atom. The spectrum is the key to the secrets of atomic structure. Before we can use this key, however, we must gather some other clues.

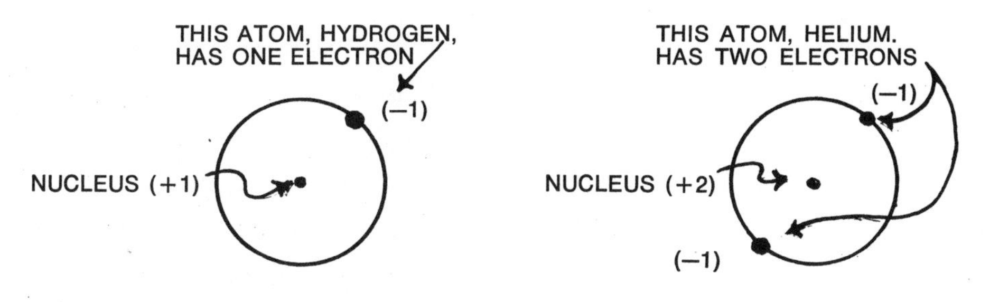

Little Solar Systems

The physicists Philipp Lenard and Ernest Rutherford gave us one clue when they showed that each atom is like a little solar system. Just as the solar system consists of a heavy mass, the sun, surrounded by planets, each atom consists of a small but heavy core called the nucleus, surrounded by electrons. Each electron carries a negative electrical charge. The nucleus carries a positive electric charge that exactly balances the charge of the electrons that surround it. If we use the charge on one electron as a unit, the total number of electrons outside the nucleus serves as a measure of the total negative charge of these electrons, and it is also a measure of the equal positive charge on the nucleus.

A Chemical Family Tree

Another clue is provided by a great discovery made nearly 100 years ago by two chemists, the Russian, Dmitri Mendeleyev, and the German, Lothar Julius Meyer. Scientists had already gathered a lot of information about the chemical elements. They had studied their physical properties, such as how hot they have to be to melt or boil, and their chemical properties, such as which other elements they combine with to form compounds. They found that some of the chemical elements were very much like each other. This made it possible to group the elements into families. For example, sodium, which is one of the two elements in ordinary table salt, belongs to the family of *alkali metals.* Magnesium, which is used in photographic flash bulbs, belongs to the family of *alkaline earths.* Chlorine, which is combined with sodium in table salt, and is also used to kill bacteria in our drinking water, belongs to the family of *halogens.*

Now here is what Meyer and Mendeleyev found. They listed the members of one chemical family, one under the other, with the lightest at the top and the heaviest at the bottom. Then they wrote alongside each name on this list the name of the next heavier element. This gave them a second list right next to the first one. *They found that the second list consisted of another family of elements.* (You can see how this worked by looking at the diagram.) By continuing this process until all families were listed, they

The Russion, Mendeleyev, and the German, Meyer, worked out a periodic table of elements.

got what is known as the *periodic table of the elements.* The periodic table of Mendeleyev and Meyer shows three important things:

1. The elements are listed in order of increasing weight, from the lightest element, hydrogen, to the heaviest element found in nature, uranium. If you count the elements in order, this gives each element a number called *the atomic number.* Hydrogen, the lightest, has atomic number one; helium, two; and so on.

2. Elements in the same vertical column belong to the same family and have similar properties.

3. The first horizontal row has two elements. The second row has eight elements, each one in a different family. The third row also has eight elements, but they belong to the same eight families as the elements of the second row.

Some Elements Misbehave

When the table was first put together, it had certain flaws that kept it from being perfect. First, to keep the families together, it was sometimes necessary to put a heavier element before a lighter one. For example, argon comes before potassium, and cobalt comes before nickel; but argon is heavier than potassium, and cobalt is heavier than nickel. Second, to keep the families together it was necessary to skip some spaces. Third, it was impossible to fit into the table a whole group of elements known as the *rare earth elements*. These were listed separately at the bottom.

Counting the Electrons

Like every scientific discovery, the periodic table suggested some new questions that ought to be answered.

Why did the weight of the atom have anything to do with its chemical properties?

Why, as you went from one atom to the next heavier one, did you keep running through the same families over and over again?

And, above all, why wasn't the table perfect?

More experiments and a new discovery helped to answer these questions. Mere *weight* was not the important thing about an atom. Something else about it determined its physical and chemical properties. What was it?

The scientists bombarded atoms with X-rays to determine the number of electrons that surround the nucleus of an atom.

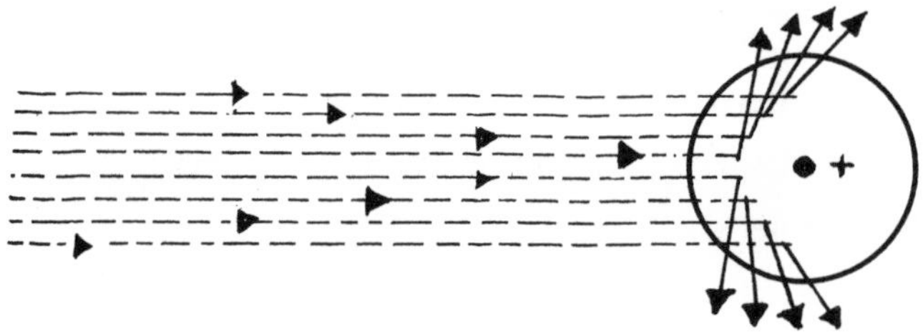

PERIODIC TABLE OF THE ELEMENTS

I	II	III	IV	V	VI	VII		VIII	
Hydrogen									2. Helium
Lithium	4. Beryllium	5. Boron	6. Carbon	7. Nitrogen	8. Oxygen	9. Fluorine			10. Neon
Sodium	12. Magnesium	13. Aluminum	14. Silicon	15. Phosphorus	16. Sulphur	17. Chlorine			18. Argon
Potassium	20. Calcium	21. Scandium	22. Titanium	23. Vanadium	24. Chromium	25. Manganese	26. Iron	27. Cobalt	28. Nickel
Copper	30. Zinc	31. Gallium	32.	33. Arsenic	34. Selenium	35. Bromine			36. Krypton
Rubidium	38. Strontium	39. Yttrium	40. conium	41. Columbium	42. Molybdenum	43. Masurium	44. Ruthenium	45. Rhodium	46. Palladium

In 1887 Germanium was discovered . . . and, one by one, the gaps in the table have been filled.

Remember that an atom is like a little solar system with a nucleus at the center and electrons revolving around it. By some very elaborate experiments, in which they bombarded atoms with the nuclei of helium atoms or with X-rays, the scientists were able to *count* the electrons surrounding the nucleus in the atoms of various elements. And they discovered a remarkable thing. The number of electrons around the nucleus of each atom was exactly equal to its atomic number, or its position in the periodic table!

Therefore, the real basis of the periodic table was not the weight of the atoms, but the number of electrons surround-

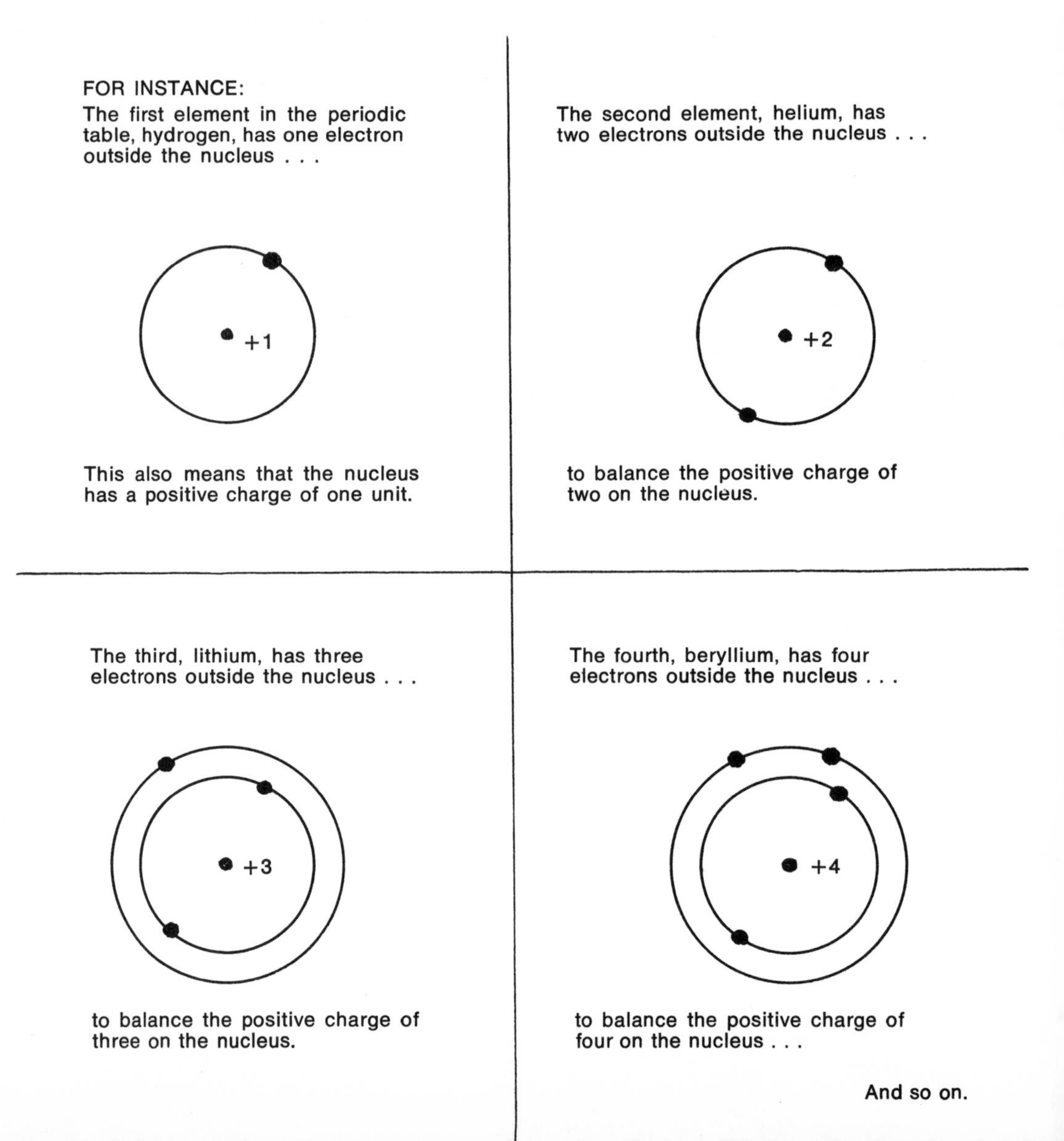

ing the nucleus—or, what amounts to the same thing, the positive charge on the nucleus. Argon comes before potassium because the argon nucleus has a charge of eighteen units and the potassium nucleus has a charge of nineteen units, even though argon is heavier than potassium. The reason why most of the table seemed to be based on weight is that a higher charge on a nucleus usually means a higher weight—but not always, as the case of argon and potassium shows. Now everything fitted!

New Elements

The flaws in the periodic table were turning out to be no flaws at all. Argon really belongs before potassium. But what about the empty spaces in the table? They, too, turned out to be not a weakness, but an important hint.

Mendeleyev himself concluded that the empty spaces indicated elements that nobody had yet discovered. He even predicted from their position in the table what their chemical and physical properties ought to be. Within a few years, gallium, germanium, and scandium *were* discovered, filling three of the blank spaces and having the properties he predicted. Since that time there has been a determined hunt for the missing elements, and, one by one, they have been found. *All the gaps in the periodic table have been filled.* Also, uranium is no longer the heaviest element, because heavier ones, neptunium, plutonium, americium, curium, berkelium, californium, einsteinium, fermium, mendelevium, nobelium, and lawrencium have been discovered.

Finally the third flaw of the table, the fact that the rare earth elements did not fit into it at all, was also explained. Clearing up this mystery, however, must wait until the next chapter.

But one important question about the periodic table still has to be answered. Why, as you go from one atom to the next in the table, do you keep running through the same families over and over again? Why does potassium, which has nineteen electrons outside the nucleus, behave very much like sodium, which has only eleven? To answer this question, it is not enough to know how many electrons surround the nucleus of each atom. We must also know how the electrons are *arranged* around the nucleus. We can answer this question if we understand the messages in the bright lines of the atom's spectrum.

Clues to Atomic Structure

Hydrogen's Telltale Lines

Let's begin to decipher the message about atoms which is carried to us in the spectrum. The natural place to start is with the simplest element, hydrogen. It is the first element in the periodic table, so it has a positive charge of one unit on its nucleus, and only one electron revolving around it. Its spectrum, as you can see in the diagram, is a simple series of lines, coming closer and closer together at one side.

Each line in the spectrum is light of a particular color. As you remember, we can measure the frequency of each color and write it down as a number. Look at the simple way the lines are arranged. Does this mean that the frequency numbers have some simple relationship, too? The physicist Balmer looked for the answer to this question, and it was as simple as 1, 2, 3, 4. Here's what he found. Take the ordinary numbers used for counting: 1, 2, 3, 4, 5. . . . Now multiply each number by itself, 1 by 1, 2 by 2, and so on. This gives you the numbers 1, 4, 9, 16, 25. . . . Next, make a series of fractions with each of these numbers in the denominator:

$$\frac{1}{1},\quad \frac{1}{4},\quad \frac{1}{9},\quad \frac{1}{16},\quad \frac{1}{25}\ldots$$

Then make a new series by subtracting each fraction later from the first one:

$$\frac{1}{1}-\frac{1}{4},\quad \frac{1}{1}-\frac{1}{9},\quad \frac{1}{1}-\frac{1}{16},\quad \frac{1}{1}-\frac{1}{25}\ldots$$

You get a similar series when you subtract each later fraction from the second one:

$$\frac{1}{4}-\frac{1}{9},\quad \frac{1}{4}-\frac{1}{16},\quad \frac{1}{4}-\frac{1}{25}\ldots$$

Balmer showed that this second series has something to do with the hydrogen spectrum.

Do you want to see what the hydrogen spectrum looks like? These numbers give you the clue. By using them you can do this experiment: On a piece of paper measure a distance of $\frac{1}{4}-\frac{1}{9}$ of a foot, or $1\frac{21}{32}$ inches from the edge, and draw a vertical line there. Now measure a distance $\frac{1}{4}-\frac{1}{16}$ of a foot, or $2\frac{1}{4}$ inches, and draw another line. Continue this way, using the numbers in the series for the distances

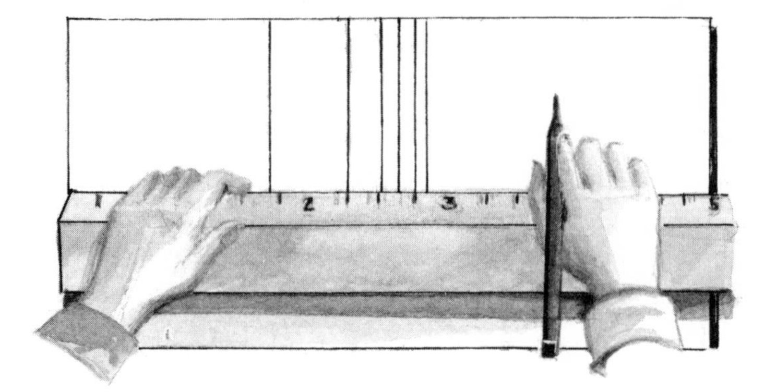

you measure. The next few distances are $2\frac{1}{2}$ inches, $2\frac{21}{32}$ inches, $2\frac{3}{4}$ inches, and $2\frac{13}{16}$ inches. The result is a series of lines that looks rather like the hydrogen spectrum. And you got it from a simple series of numbers!

Balmer's discovery showed that there is a special set of numbers belonging to the hydrogen atom, and the frequency of each bit of light sent out by the atom is the difference between two of these numbers. This was the first link in a chain of discoveries, and as we move along the chain we'll see more and more how important it was.

The next link was supplied by another physicist, Ritz. He showed that every element has a special set of such numbers, and that the frequency of every line in its spectrum is the difference between two of the numbers. These numbers were named after him—*Ritz terms*.

The third link was supplied by a fact based on the work of the famous physicist, Planck. Remember that he was one of the discoverers of those little bundles of light called photons. It was found that the frequency of a photon is a measure of the amount of energy it contains. So, if the frequency of a photon released by an atom is the difference between two Ritz terms, that must mean that the energy released by the atom is the difference between two Ritz terms. Hidden in this last statement is the clue which still another scientist, Niels Bohr, used to figure out what the atom must be like to send out light the way it does.

The Model That Didn't Work Right

Suppose we try now to see just what the hydrogen atom is like. At the center is the nucleus, with a positive charge. A single electron, attracted by the nucleus, revolves around it. We might be tempted to compare the revolving of the electron to the kind of vibrating electric current that sends out radio waves. Then, with each trip the electron makes around the nucleus, it would send out a wave. The frequency of the light sent out would then be the frequency with which the electron make its trips around the nucleus. This sounds like a simple theory that would explain why atoms send out light. But it doesn't fit the facts. First, if it is the revolving of the electron that accounts for the broadcasting of light, then the atom should be sending out light all the time. But this is not true. Atoms send out light only when they are in a condition known as the *excited state.*

Secondly, as the electron revolves, if it kept on sending out light, it would be losing energy and would slow down. The effect would be like what happens when you play a phonograph record with a hand-wound spring motor. When the record begins to slow down, the sound coming from the record, which may have been a high soprano, begins to go down the scale all the way to a deep bass. If the electron slowed down in the same way, the light it sends out would go down the scale of frequencies, getting lower and lower without skipping any. The spectrum would then be a continuous band of light like the rainbow. But we know it isn't like that at all.

The Electron Climbs the Steps

Think about this model that doesn't work. What should a good model of the atom do? It should explain why the atom doesn't send out light all the time. It should explain what the excited state really is. It should explain the meaning of the Ritz terms, and why only certain frequencies appear in the spectrum. And all this is just what Bohr's theory of the atom does. Here it is.

In order to lift a ball off the ground, you must pull against the force of gravity that tends to pull the ball back to the ground. The work you do in opposing this force is stored up in the ball as hidden energy. If you drop the ball so that it falls to the ground, the hidden energy is released and appears in the form of the *bounce* when the ball strikes the ground. The higher you lift the ball, the more energy you give it, and the bigger the bounce when it hits the ground. Each height of the ball therefore represents a definite level of energy.

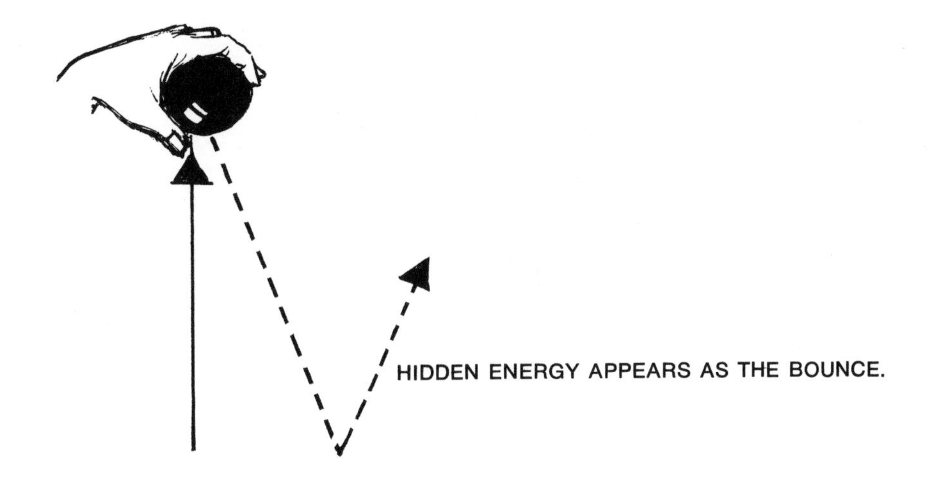

Now put the ball on a flight of steps. Each step, since it is at a different height above the ground, represents a different energy level. If the ball falls from one step to another, it goes from a higher energy level to a lower one. The hidden energy that it loses in the fall, shows up as the bounce when the ball hits the lower step. This is the difference between the two energy levels.

Bohr explained that the Ritz terms were a series of energy steps on which the electron may rest. While it stays on the lowest level, no light is sent out. An electric current can push it to a higher level, the excited state. Then when it

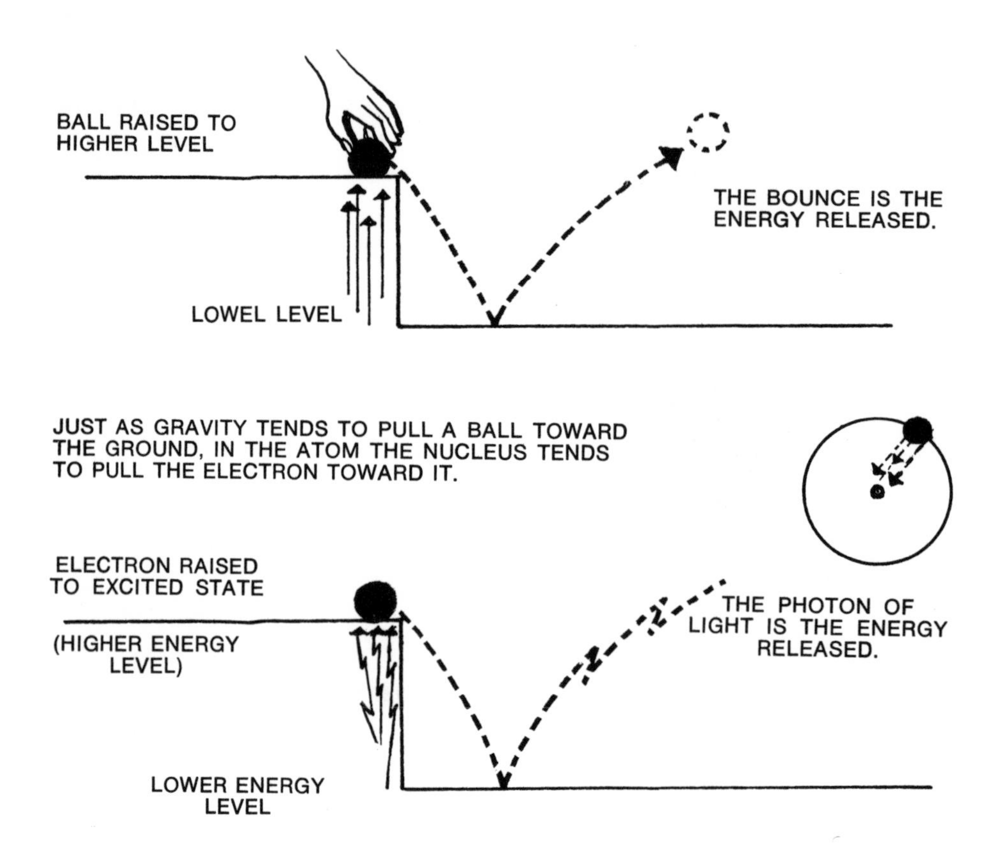

falls from the higher level to a lower level, it loses energy, and the lost energy is released as a photon of light, just as the ball's energy was released as a bounce. The photon of light then shows up as a line in the spectrum. The Ritz terms of an atom are the energy levels of the atom. That is why the frequency or energy of every line in the spectrum is the difference between two Ritz terms.

By using this theory of energy steps in the atom, Bohr could give a simple picture of what the hydrogen atom is like. He showed mathematically that the electron is not free to travel in any old orbit around the nucleus, but that only certain orbits are possible. These orbits are the energy steps of the atom. The smallest possible orbit is so tiny that over 250 *million* of them placed side by side would cover a distance of only *one inch*. The second orbit that is possible is four times as wide as the smallest. The third orbit is nine times as wide as the smallest. The fourth one is sixteen times as wide, and so on. You see here our old friends, the numbers 1, 4, 9, 16, 25 . . . in Balmer's series.

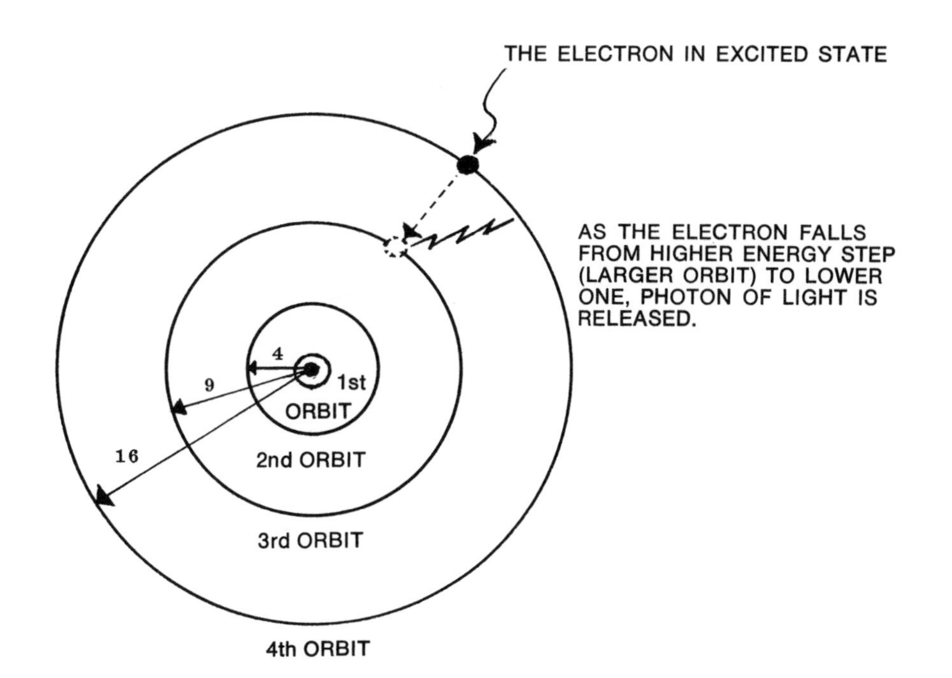

When the electron is traveling in the smallest orbit, it has the lowest amount of hidden energy. While it stays in this orbit, it does not send out light. →

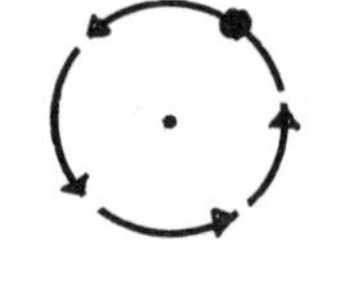

By the use of heat or an electric current, it can be pushed out of this orbit into one of the larger orbits where it will have more energy. When the electron is in one of the larget orbits, the atom is in the excited state. →

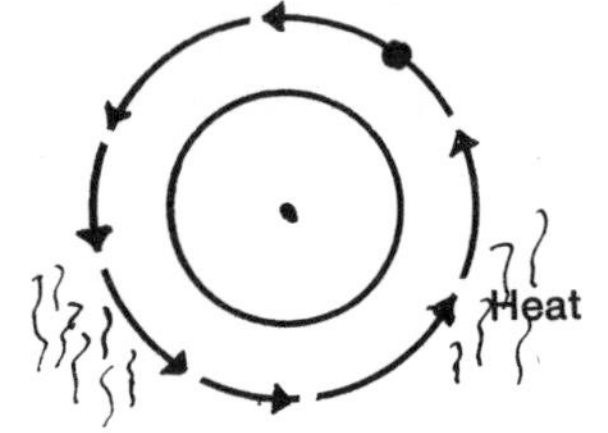

Responding to the attraction of the positive charge on the nucleus, the electron jumps back again to the lower orbit, just as a ball thrown into the air falls back again to the ground. The extra energy it had in the excited state is released as a photon of light. →

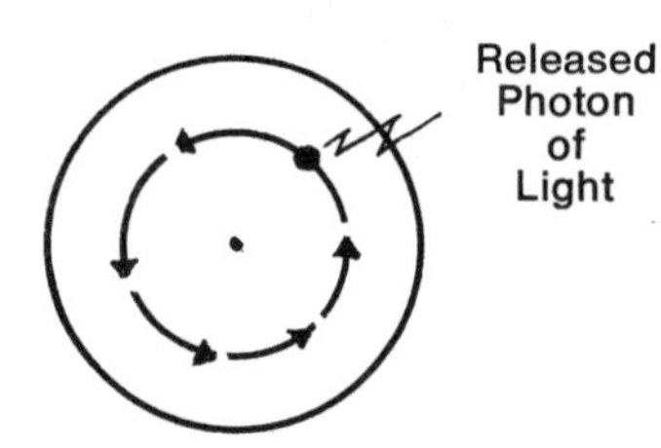

This picture of the hydrogen atom was the fourth link in the chain of discoveries that opened up the secrets of atomic structure.

The Wandering Orbit

The fifth link was provided by the use of more accurate instruments for studying the spectrum. With their help, close examination of the lines in the spectrum showed that each line is actually a cluster of fine lines that are very close together. This is called the *fine structure* of the spectrum, and within it lies another clue.

The first series of lines showed that there are energy steps in the atom. The fact that each line is itself made up of a series of fine lines shows, in the same way, that each step is made up of smaller steps.

FOR EACH SIZE OF ORBIT SEVERAL SHAPES ARE POSSIBLE.

The energy of the big steps is connected with the motion of the electron and its orbit around the nucleus. But what motion accounts for the energy of the small steps? Still another scientist, Arnold Sommerfeld, supplied the answer: For each orbit of a particular *size,* several *shapes* are possible, ranging all the way from circles to narrow ellipses. When the orbit is an ellipse, the nucleus is not at the center but at a point to one side known as the focus. When an electron in a narrow elliptical orbit comes close to the nucleus, it picks up speed. According to the theory of relativity, as you will see in Chapter Eleven, this makes it temporarily heavier. As a result, it gets a jolt which shifts its orbit a little bit. While the electron revolves about the nucleus in the elliptical orbit, the orbit itself keeps shifting and rotating. This rotation gives the electron a definite amount of energy, which depends on how close the electron comes to the nucleus. Since in a narrow ellipse the electron will come closer to the nucleus than in an ellipse that is more nearly circular, the energy of the rotation of the orbit depends on the *shape* of the orbit. The meaning of the small energy steps is that not all shapes are possible, but only a few definite ones. For orbits of the smallest size only one shape is possible. For orbits of the second size two shapes are possible. For orbits of the third size three shapes are possible, and so on.

THE ELECTRON MOVES IN SHIFTING ORBIT:

1

2

3

4

5

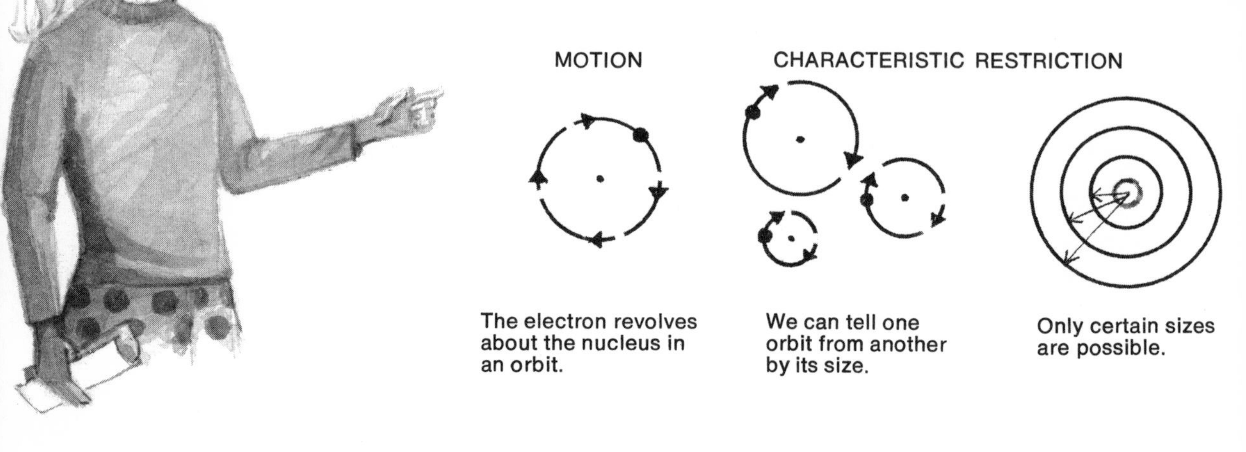

We have now gone far enough to understand better the meaning of lines in the spectrum. A series of lines shows the existence of energy steps in the atom. The energy steps show the existence of

- a *motion* in the atom,
- a *characteristic* by which we can tell one motion from another,
- a *restriction* of the motion to certain cases only.

FINE STRUCTURE OF LINES REVEALS:

MOTION | CHARACTERISTIC | RESTRICTION

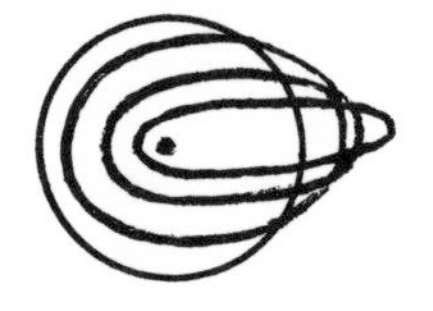

The orbit itself rotates.

We can tell one case from another by the shape of the orbit.

Only certain shapes are possible.

If we find more lines — and we shall — we shall have to look for more motions, characteristics, and restrictions.

The Wobbling Atom

Could those lines in the spectrum show still more about the atom? Another experiment supplied the sixth link in the chain of discovery. When glowing hydrogen atoms were placed between the poles of a magnet, each line in the spectrum split up into several lines. This is called the *Zeeman effect*. The lines split in much the same way when the atoms were placed in an electric field. This is called the *Stark effect*. This splitting showed that when the atom is in an electrical or magnetic field, some new energy steps are created.

So far the picture of the atom looks rather like a spinning top. When you spin a top on the ground, it is being acted on by a force, the force of gravity. Try it, and you will notice that when the axis of the top is tilted, the top will wobble as

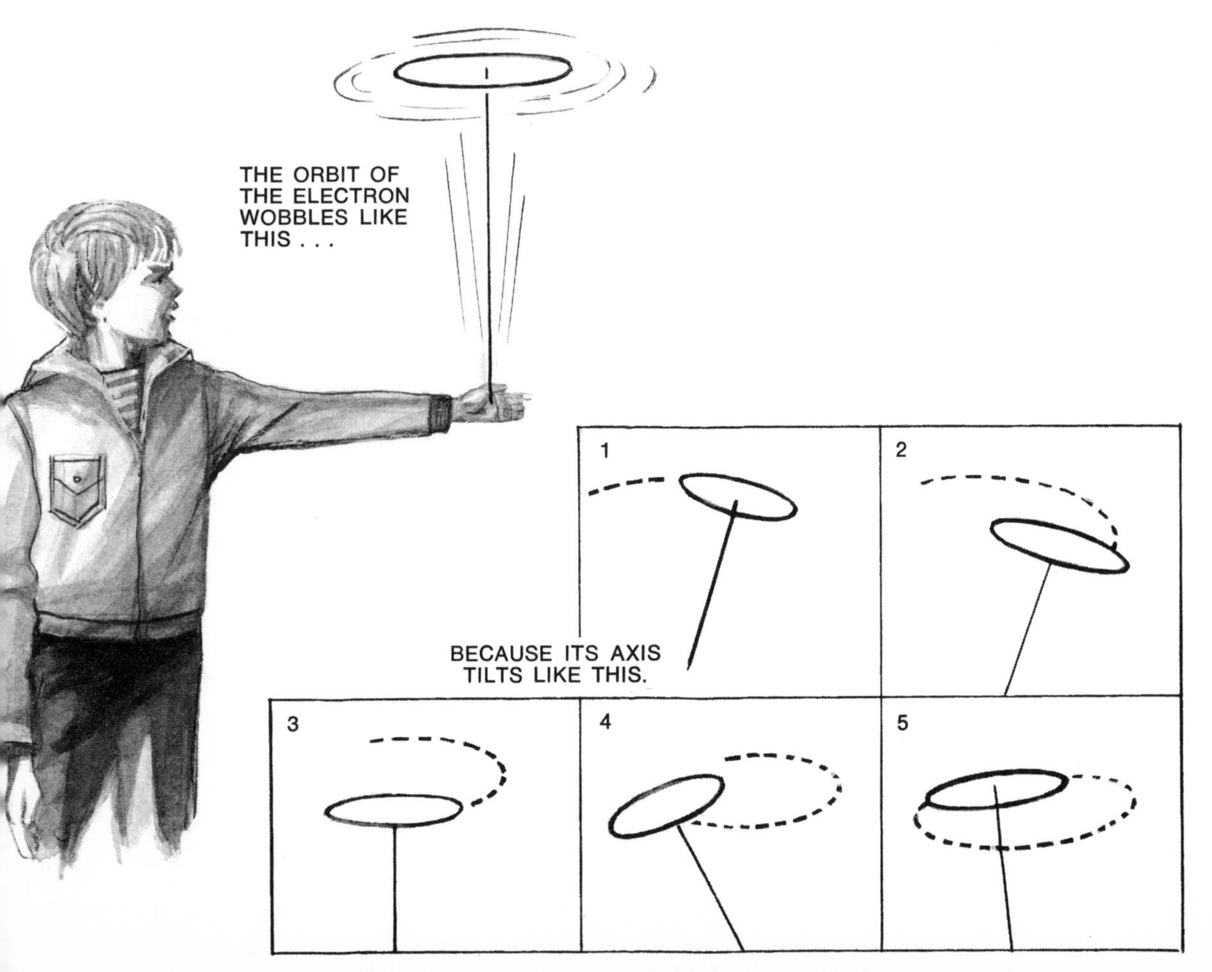

it spins around the axis. The more it tilts, the more it wobbles. The same thing happens to an atom in an electric or magnetic field. The orbit of the electron wobbles. But it does not wobble just any old way. Only certain tilts are possible. And the number of possible tilts depends on the shape and size of the orbit. The wider orbits, which can have more shapes, can also have more tilts.

The Electron Takes a Spin

A seventh and last link so far in the chain of discovery came from the study of the spectra of sodium and potassium. These spectra showed double lines, where we would expect single ones. And these double lines, as you can now guess, meant still more energy steps. What kind of motion accounted for them? We have already found three kinds of motion in the atom: The electron revolves around the nucleus in an orbit; the orbit itself rotates; and the orbit may wobble. What other motion is possible? The answer is that the electron itself spins like a top, the way the earth spins around its axis. Only two spins are possible—in opposite directions.

From a chain of seven discoveries growing out of the study of the spectrum, we have learned about four motions in the atom, and the energy steps associated with them. They are listed in the chart below.

The Clue in the Spectrum		The Motion it Reveals		The Energy Steps Associated With It
1. The Balmer lines	→	Revolution around the nucleus	→	Possible sizes of the orbit
2. The fine structure	→	Rotation of the orbit	→	Possible shapes of the orbit
3. The Zeeman or Stark effect	→	Wobbling of the orbit	→	Possible tilts of the orbit
4. The double lines	→	Spin of the electron	→	2 possible directions of spin

The Electron Gets a Permanent Wave

The picture we now have of the atom explains many of the known facts remarkably well, as we shall see. However, other facts remained unexplained. This led to the development of a new picture called *quantum* mechanics, based on a revolutionary idea. The Frenchman, Louis de Broglie, suggested that, just as light travels as a corpuscle as well as a wave, the electron travels as a wave as well as a corpuscle. That this is true has been proved by experiments in which electrons have been fired through crystals. The orderly arrangement of the atoms in the crystal behaves like the scratched lines on a grating. The result was a series of interference bands, showing that the electrons must travel in waves. When the motion of an electron is confined to a closed space, as it is in the hydrogen atom, the result is a stationary wave like the vibration of a tight string when it is plucked. As you know if you have ever watched a vibrating string, it can have two or more points that do not move. These are called *nodes*. In quantum mechanics the problem of finding all possible energy levels of the atom becomes the problem of finding all possible combinations of nodes.

This new picture of the atom fits the facts better than the one we just built up out of four motions in the atom. However, the new picture is more difficult to understand without the use of mathematics. The old picture, though less accurate, is easier to see, so we shall hold onto it for the rest of this discussion.

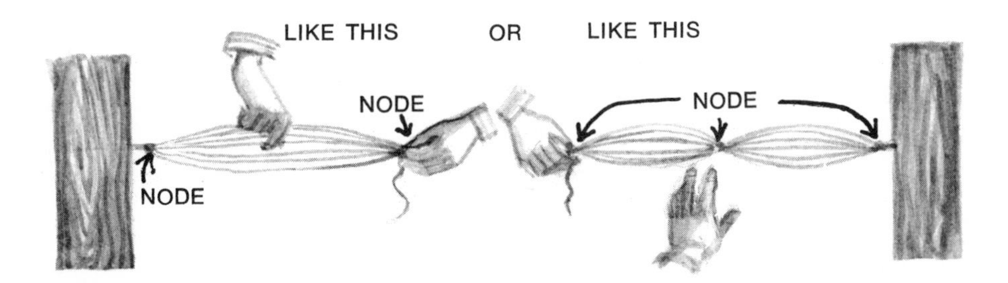

Portrait of the Atom

Building Up the Elements

We now know enough about the atom to show how the electrons are arranged around the nucleus, and to explain the arrangement of the elements in the periodic table.

Let's begin with hydrogen, as we did before. The hydrogen nucleus has a positive charge of one unit. This charge is balanced by a single electron. In the unexcited state, this electron will be in the orbit of lowest energy—the orbit of smallest size.

Now let's take an atom with a nucleus that has a positive charge of two units. This must be balanced by a second electron. Where can we put it? The physicist Pauli found that no two electrons can be on the same energy step. So we have to put it on the next higher step. This will also be an orbit of the smallest size. The two electrons will be the same distance from the nucleus, but they will spin in opposite directions. This element is helium.

As you remember, the smallest orbit can have only one shape and one position in a field of force. So it has room for only the two electrons with opposite spins. But suppose the nucleus of an atom has a charge of three or more. Where do the other electrons go? They will have to be farther away from the nucleus, in larger orbits. All the electrons with orbits the same size are said to be in the same *shell* around the nucleus, so the two innermost electrons make up the first shell. Electrons with larger orbits will, therefore, have to go into a second shell.

An atom, whose nucleus has a charge of three, has two electrons in the first shell and one in the second shell. But let's keep going. As we keep on increasing the charge on the nucleus, we can keep adding electrons to the second shell until it, too, has been filled up.

Let's see how many electrons go into the second shell:

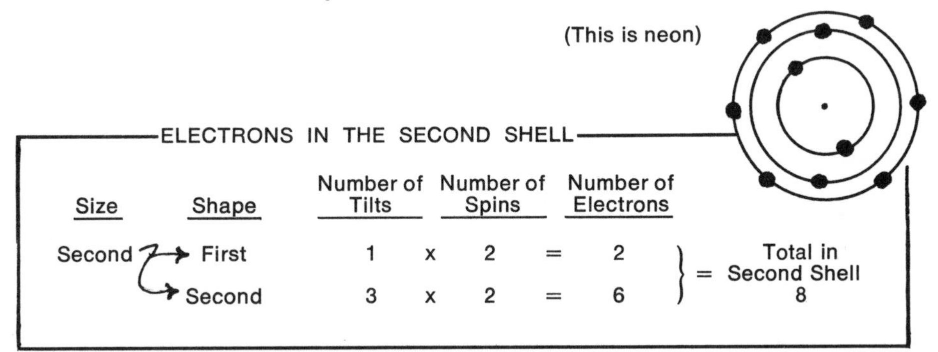

ELECTRONS IN THE SECOND SHELL

Size	Shape	Number of Tilts		Number of Spins		Number of Electrons	
Second	First	1	x	2	=	2	= Total in Second Shell 8
	Second	3	x	2	=	6	

The two electrons of the first shape form a subshell. The six electrons of the second shape form another subshell.

The elements with electrons in the second shell, listed in order, are these: lithium, beryllium, boron, carbon, nitrogen, oxygen, fluorine, and neon. In neon the charge on the nucleus is 10, and it is surrounded by two complete shells of electrons.

But what happens if the charge on the nucleus is higher than ten? Now there has to be a third shell of electrons. In this shell, the orbits are of the third size:

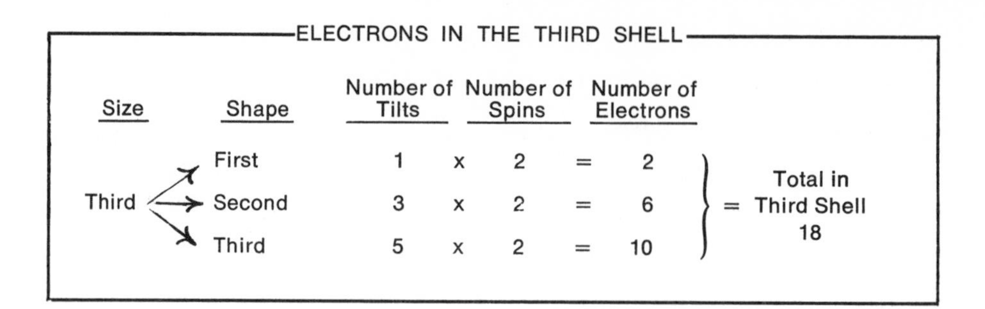

ELECTRONS IN THE THIRD SHELL

Size	Shape	Number of Tilts		Number of Spins		Number of Electrons	
Third	First	1	x	2	=	2	= Total in Third Shell 18
	Second	3	x	2	=	6	
	Third	5	x	2	=	10	

This is the sodium atom

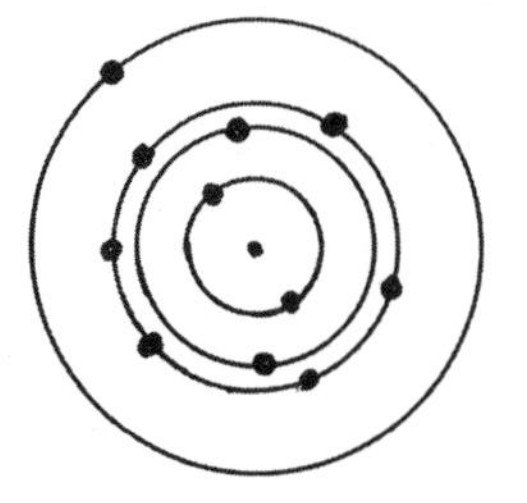

This is the magnesium atom

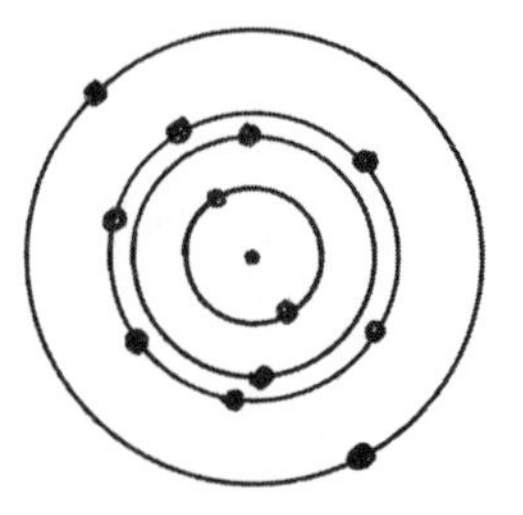

The third shell has room for three subshells made up of two, six, and ten electrons each.

The first eight elements formed in this way are sodium, magnesium, aluminum, silicon, phosphorus, sulfur, chlorine, and argon. Chemically and physically, they are like the eight elements we got when we filled up the second shell.

You might think we could just keep going until we built up the whole periodic table, but from here on there is a change. *We don't always complete an inner shell before putting electrons into an outer shell.* This strange change occurs because sometimes a large orbit that is very narrow has a lower energy level than a smaller orbit that is wide. And the fixed rule is that the electron always goes into the lowest energy level that has not yet been filled. For this reason, we get the next element, potassium, not by putting a ninth electron into the third shell, but by putting one electron into the *fourth* shell. The table shows you how the atoms of the next twelve elements are put together.

And so it goes until we get lawrencium with a nuclear charge of 103, and 103 electrons arranged in shells around it.

Element	Total Number of Electrons	Number of Electrons in First Shell	Second Shell	Third Shell	Fourth Shell
Calcium	20	2	8	8	2
Scandium	21	2	8	9	2
Titanium	22	2	8	10	2
Vanadium	23	2	8	11	2
Chromium	24	2	8	12	1
Manganese	25	2	8	13	2
Iron	26	2	8	14	2
Cobalt	27	2	8	15	2
Nickel	28	2	8	16	2
Copper	29	2	8	18	1
Zinc	30	2	8	18	2
Gallium	31	2	8	18	3

Why Elements Behave As They Do

We have just built up the elements in the order of their atomic numbers, the way they appear in the periodic table. But more than that, because we now know that the electrons that surround the nucleus are arranged in shells around the nucleus, we can explain the chemical behavior of each element.

First: An element that has only completed shells, like helium or argon, is very stable. It does not tend to lose or to capture electrons, and therefore does not tend to combine with other elements. That is why these elements are called the *inert gases.*

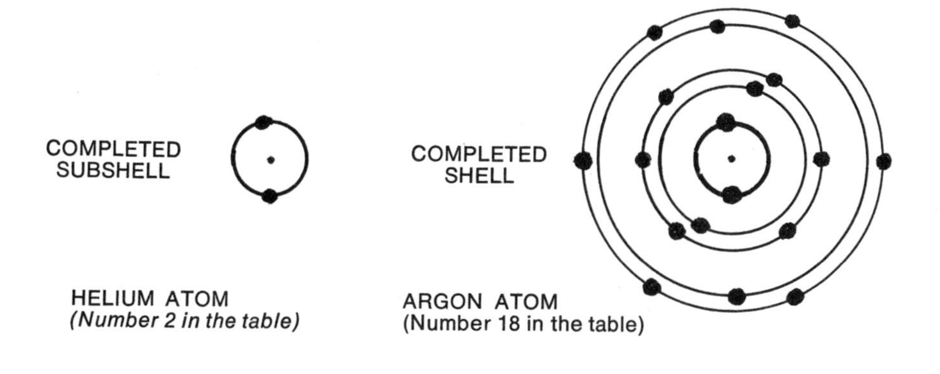

HELIUM ATOM
(Number 2 in the table)

ARGON ATOM
(Number 18 in the table)

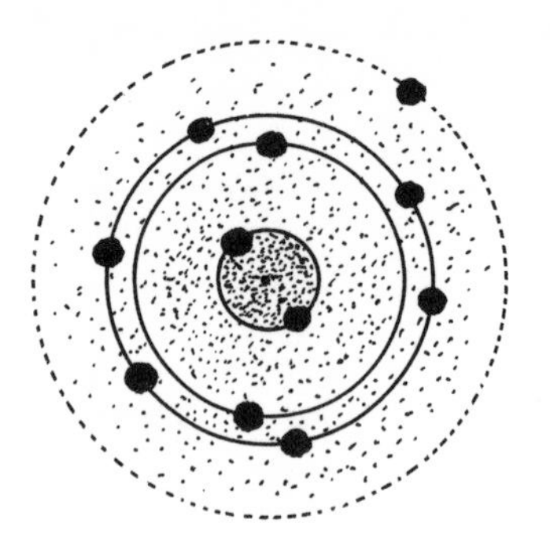

THE SINGLE ELECTRON IN THE OUTER SHELL IS LOOSELY HELD BECAUSE THE NUCLEUS IN THIS ATOM (SODIUM, AN ALKALI METAL) IS SCREENED BY THE INNER SHELLS.

Second: An element that has only one electron outside an inner shell can lose that electron very easily. This is so because the inner shells screen the nucleus and reduce its attraction for the outer electron, which is therefore held very loosely and is easily lost. This is characteristic of sodium and potassium and the whole family of alkali metals to which they belong. In combining with other elements they tend to lose one electron.

Since beryllium and magnesium have only two electrons that are outside the inner shells, they tend to lose two electrons when they combine with other elements. This is characteristic of the family they belong to, the alkaline earths.

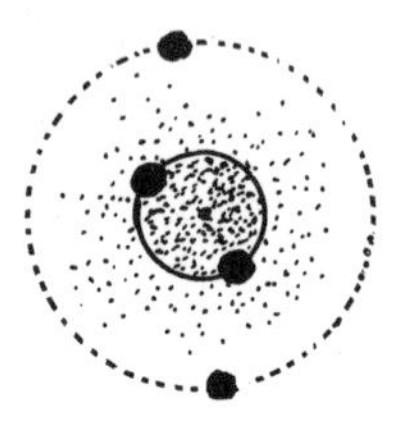

THIS ATOM (BERYLLIUM) TENDS TO LOSE ITS TWO OUTER ELECTRONS BECAUSE THEY ARE LOOSELY HELD BY THE NUCLEUS WHICH IS SCREENED BY THE INNER SHELL.

Third: An element like fluorine or chlorine, which lacks only one electron to complete a shell or a subshell, tends to capture an electron from another element in chemical combination. This is characteristic of the family that they belong to, the halogens. It is natural that the alkali metals combine easily with the halogens, since one supplies the electron that the other lacks. When sodium combines with chlorine, the result is ordinary table salt.

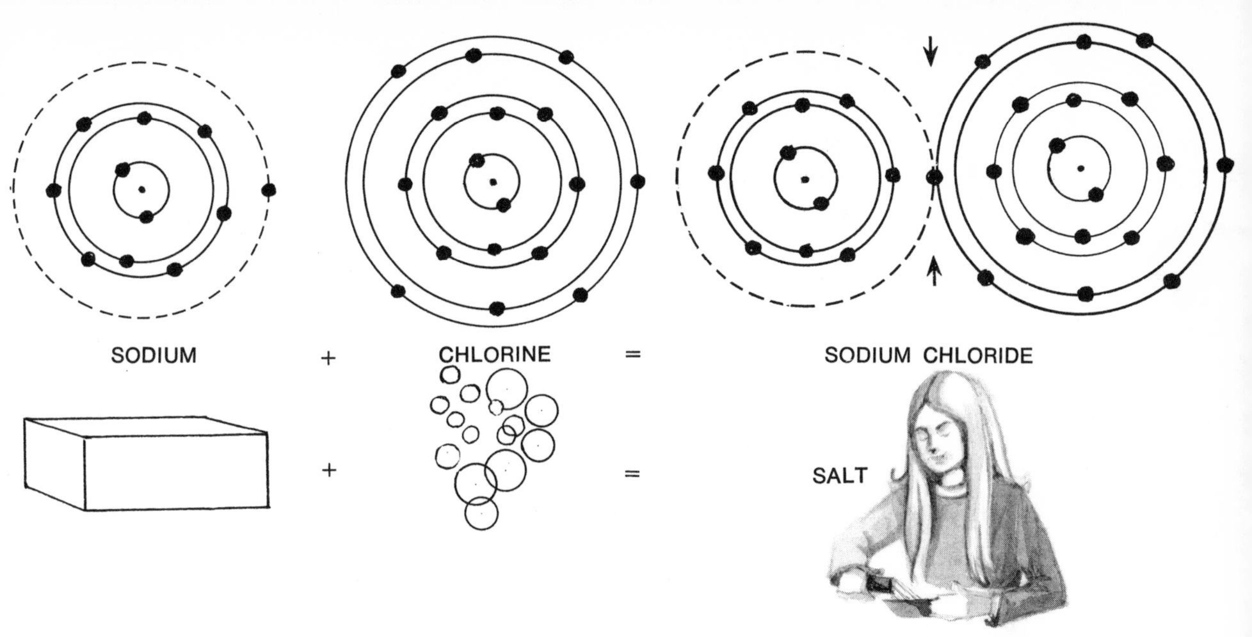

Fourth: Carbon, which has four electrons in a half-completed shell, can either lose the four, or capture four more. More often, carbon and another element will share their outer electrons so that each helps the other complete the outer shell or subshell. This explains why it enters into so many compounds, and is in all those compounds which are called *organic*.

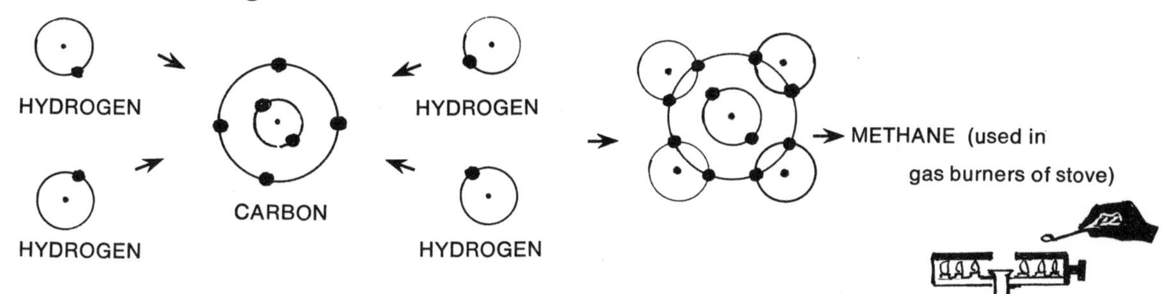

We Learned It All from Light

Our questions are answered. We have built up the whole periodic table, and everything fits. The flaws are no longer flaws. Also, we have found out a lot about what goes on inside the atom. We have uncovered the secret of atomic structure.

How did we find out? By learning how to read and understand the lines of light in the spectrum. Light brought us these messages from the inner world of the atom.

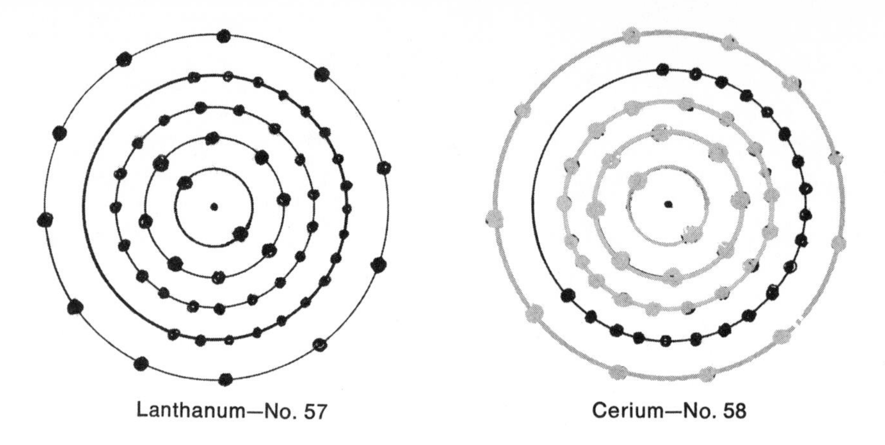
Lanthanum—No. 57 Cerium—No. 58

Fourteen that Look Alike

We have one more thing to explain. Why don't the rare earths fit into the periodic table? The element just before the rare earths, lanthanum, has an atomic number of 57. It has two electrons in the first shell, which is complete; eight electrons in the second shell, which is complete; eighteen electrons in the third shell, which is complete; eighteen electrons in the fourth shell, which is incomplete; and eleven electrons in the fifth shell.

The next fourteen elements are the rare earths. They are formed by gradually filling in the fourteen gaps in the fourth shell. Since there are already eleven electrons in the fifth shell, all fourteen of the rare earths have them.

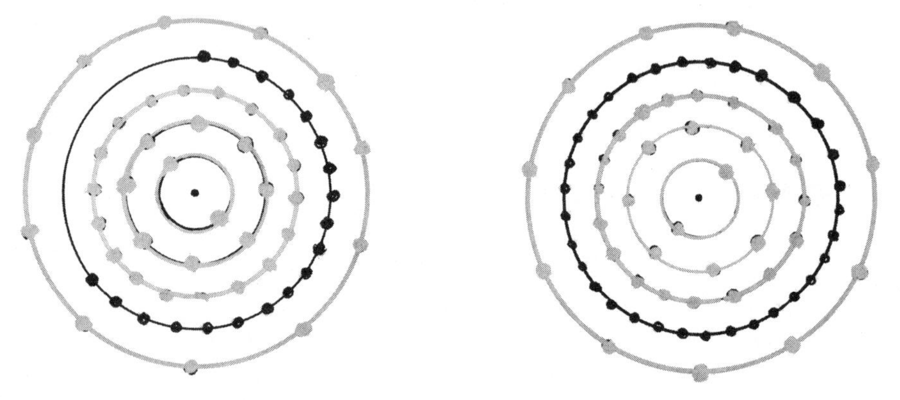
Praesodymium—No. 59 . . . and so on through Lutetium, No. 71.

Since the chemical properties of an element depend mostly on how many electrons are in the outer shells, all fourteen of the rare earths are very much like each other and form a separate family by themselves.

What Good Is a Theory?

The first scientists to investigate atomic structure were like wanderers in a valley surrounded by unexplored mountains. They could see the mountains nearest them and the peaks of one or two others beyond, but they knew very little about the entire range. Yet in this book, with the help of the modern theory of atomic structure, we have climbed one of the highest peaks and we see the whole range laid out before our eyes. We see not only separate facts, like the spectra of the elements and the meaning of the Ritz terms, but also how one fact leads to another and how together they make a complete picture. And, far off in the distance, we catch sight of things we couldn't even dream of in the valley.

Let's stop and rest here on our mountain peak, where we can look around, before we start on our next adventure with light. As we glance back at the road we have just traveled, we see that we have been examining the *theory* of atomic structure. We see how one discovery was built on another until we finally got a whole theory—a theory which answered our questions and helped us to understand the facts we discovered. Without theories there would be no science, so it is important to know how theories grow and what man can do with them. The theory of atomic structure is a good example.

While other animals use things pretty much as they find them in nature, man for thousands of years has been changing the world to suit his own purposes. To do this, he learned to work, first with his bare hands, and then with tools. And as he worked, he learned more and more about the world he lived in. While he was smelting metal, getting dyestuffs from plants, tanning leather, and making glass and pottery, he was also discovering many facts about the chemical nature of the world. These facts, which he gathered in the course of his practical work, became the foundation of modern chemistry.

But a mass of facts alone can be as bewildering as unexplored mountains towering above you in the valley. To understand how facts are connected with each other and what they really mean, you need a scientific theory. With the help of a correct theory, the facts can be made to fit together like the pieces of a jigsaw puzzle. The modern theory of atomic structure did this for the facts of chemistry, by fitting them into and explaining the periodic table of the elements.

The modern theory of atomic structure did more than explain the known facts. It also led to the discovery of new facts, like the existence of unknown elements, that filled the gaps in the periodic table and even extended it. Here is another important way men use scientific theory. Like a beacon, it lights up unexplored regions of nature and helps us to make new discoveries.

But that isn't all. Because the atomic theory helps man to understand chemistry far better than before, he can now do many more things with nature. There was a time when the words, *organic chemicals,* meant things that could be obtained only from plants and animals. Now the nature of these chemicals is understood so well that many, like the vitamins, can be made in laboratories. New substances, not found in nature, like the plastics, are actually being created. Old enemies, like the disease germs, are being conquered. Whole inustries have been built up on the basis of the modern theory of atomic structure. The theory, which grew out of man's practical work, in turn, has made possible new and better work, new and better ways of changing nature

"A LEVER IS A SIMPLE MACHINE USED TO INCREASE FORCE OR SPEED."
"ALL LEVERS OF THE FIRST CLASS HAVE THEIR FULCRUM BETWEEN THE EFFORT AND THE RESISTANCE."
"A WHEEL AND AXLE MAY BE CONSIDERED A CONTINUOUS LEVER OF THE FIRST CLASS."
A THEORY HELPS YOU TO TAKE SEPARATE FACTS AND TO PUT THEM TOGETHER TO HAVE A NEW USE AND MEANING.

The atomic theory we have just summarized dealt with the arrangement of the electrons surrounding the nucleus of the atom. Once this problem was solved, the way was clear for the next big step forward in the study of the atom—cracking the nucleus itself. Here, too, science has increased man's power over nature, giving him, this time, the power of atomic energy. What changes this great power will make in the way men live, still remains to be seen, because the serious study of the atomic nucleus has only just begun. But we do have proofs of its wonderful possibilities in the use of atomic energy to run submarines or to operate electric power stations.

As we stand on the mountain peak which we have just climbed, guided by modern atomic theory, we see the facts of chemistry in orderly array. We see men climbing the mountains of knowledge, advancing their practical work of changing the world, their path lit up by scientific theory.

The progress of science is not easy, nor does it always travel forward in a straight line. For man to make the discoveries we have been discussing, he had first of all to cast off the chains of ignorance and superstition, which kept him from examining the real world and seeing it as it is. Sometimes, too, man's knowledge has been distorted and misused—used to confuse people and even to destroy what they have already built. Then progress has been slow and painful.

But whenever man's knowledge of nature has been put to work to improve the life of mankind, it has moved ahead. Nature has no secret that will be forever closed to mankind. However, while every advance of science solves old problems, it uncovers new ones. Man's knowledge of the world will never be complete. It will always be enlarging and unfolding.

Light in Disguise

We have made light do so much work for us that you may think you are completely its master. But this is far from true. In fact, if we look at what light does in its most common form—sunlight—we find that by its coming and going it regulates our lives. We wake up when it comes in the daytime, and we go to sleep when it leaves at night. When it comes north, we swelter and sweat in the summertime. When it goes south in the wintertime, we freeze.

The Real Weatherman

We call the man who predicts the weather "the weatherman." But the real weatherman is light because it *makes* the weather. It is the action of sunlight pouring in on the earth that causes all the different changes of weather. By making the ground hot, sunlight causes the air to get warmer and rise. At the same time, through evaporation, it raises tons of water out of the ocean into the air. Here we discover another important fact about light. It not only appears in the form of radiant energy, traveling through space in the form of electromagnetic waves, but it may also have many disguises. The energy of sunlight is changed into new forms. It becomes the energy in the movement of water ready to fall as rain. It flashes out as the energy of lightning, jumping from cloud to cloud or to the ground. Now light may be disguised as a gentle breeze, later as a violent thunderstorm. Here it may be a blizzard, there a flood, yonder a hurricane.

Rainmakers

For centuries man has been almost helpless before the weather. His ships have been destroyed by storms, his crops have been burned by drought. He can cushion the shock of bad weather by irrigation and forest windbreaks, but he has not been able to choose the weather he wants. However, all this may soon change. We have been learning more and more about the forces that make the weather. And such knowledge is power. It is no longer true, as Mark Twain once said, that "everybody talks about the weather but nobody does anything about it." The City of New York, struggling against a severe water shortage, decided to stop waiting for rain. Instead it launched a program of *making* rain. This was a first step in a new phase of man's study of the weather. From now on we won't be content with merely predicting the weather, we shall try to make it.

Will actions like weather-making free us from the rule of sunlight? The answer is no and yes. Since we are part of the world of nature, we shall always be influenced by natural forces. But the more we learn about these natural forces, the more we can direct their influence for our own benefit. We can use the power of light. Man can form a working partnership with nature.

Light's Hiding Places

Do you see that reservoir of water? Light is hiding there. The radiant energy of sunlight raised the water out of the ocean and let it fall on the mountains as rain and snow. As long as the water stays on the mountains, some of the energy it got from the sun is still hidden within it, ready to do work as it falls to sea level. It can turn turbines, which in turn will transform it into electrical energy.

Do you see that steam engine? Light is hiding there. Thousands of years ago sunlight made giant ferns grow in the swamp. The energy of the sunlight was stored in these ferns in the form of chemical energy. Great changes in the surface of the earth buried these ferns, and compressed them into what we call coal. But the chemical energy is still there, ready to be released when the coal is burned. Thus the sunlight, hidden underground for thousands of years, re-

appears in the coal fires we make to boil the water to make the steam that makes the engines run.

Sometimes light comes at our bidding. But sometimes it comes unasked, and by the damage it does, reminds us that we still have a lot to learn. Do you see that forest fire? Light is hiding there. Working through the green leaves of trees, it made wood out of carbon dioxide and water. Its energy, coming out of the burning wood, causes the great flames that the men are trying so desperately to control.

There are many forms of energy: light, heat, motion, chemical energy, electricity, magnetism, and gravitation. Each may be transformed into every other. They are all different forms of one and the same thing. Since all things contain energy in one form or another, light is hiding in them all.

Giver of Life

Light has one more hiding place that will probably surprise you most. It is hiding in—*you!* The energy that keeps you alive comes from food. The food comes from animals and plants. And the animals got *their* food from plants. So all your food came from plants in the first place. But the energy that made the plants grow all came from sunlight. So there you have it—light is not only in the things around us. It is in you, and in me, and in everybody.

Exploring the Universe

You Can't Catch Light

Light travels so fast that there is nothing else that moves fast enough to keep up with it. That, in itself, would explain why it is impossible to catch up with a beam of light. But actually, the situation is much worse. If an automobile goes down the road at a speed of forty miles an hour, and you chase it in another car traveling thirty miles an hour, you won't catch up with it. But at least you will reduce the speed at which the auto is getting away from you to ten miles an hour. But the American physicist, Albert A. Michelson, who tried to chase light, got an entirely different result. His experience showed that, no matter how fast you chase a beam of light, it does not reduce the speed at which the light escapes from you. The light still gets away from you at the same speed—186,000 miles per second. It's as if your feet were slipping and you made no progress in the chase at all! This startling fact became the foundation of Einstein's theory of relativity.

The Rubber Yardstick

Once the scientists got used to this strange fact about the speed of light, they were ready to change their ideas about many things. And they had to. Because the theory of relativity leads to some very strange results. One of them is that the length of a yardstick isn't a fixed thing, but depends on how fast it is moving. Suppose that John and Mary are moving at the same speed, each one carrying a yardstick. They compare their yardsticks and find that they are the same length. Now suppose that John keeps on moving at the same speed, but Mary starts moving away at a greatly increased speed. If John measures Mary's yardstick as it moves away from him, he finds that it is now shorter than his. In fact, the faster it moves, the shorter it is. At ordinary

speeds this shrinking is too small to be noticed, so you won't get a chance to see it yourself. It would be noticeable only at speeds that are close to the speed of light.

It was very hard for scientists to accept this idea at first, because it didn't fit in with their idea of a unit of measure that was always the same. A yard was supposed to be fixed and unchanging no matter what the circumstances. But when an idea is contradicted by a fact, the fact has to win.

In this case, the fact established by Michelson's experiment, that the speed of light is the same for all observers (no matter how fast they try to chase it), drove out of scientific thinking the old idea of an abstract unit of measure that never changed. You will see what this meant if you think about it this way: Measurements are not made in the abstract. A real yard is measured with a real yardstick. And yardsticks are no exception to the rule that everything in the universe changes with the conditions of its existence. In this case, the length of the yardstick changes with the speed of its motion.

The mathematical equations of the theory of relativity say that the faster an object moves past you, the shorter it gets. Suppose we use the equations to answer the question: "What happens to the length of an object when it moves with the speed of light?" The equations tell us that if an object ever got to move as fast as light does, it would shrink down to nothing at all. This sounds fantastic—and it is!

Now you may well ask, "Isn't there something wrong with a theory that gives a fantastic answer to a question?" No, there isn't. What the equations are telling us here, is that the question itself was fantastic. In reality, the only thing that travels as fast as light is—light itself. And no real object, with mass, can ever travel that fast. The theory of relativity tells us why this is true. The equations show that the faster an object moves, the heavier it gets. And the heavier it gets, the harder it is to make it move faster! So you needn't worry about your yardstick—or any other object—ever shrinking away to nothing.

Everybody Is in the Act

In a children's theater, the children became so excited about what they saw on the stage that they called out to the

actors, telling them what to do next. The actors talked to the children, as though it were all part of the show, and even followed their suggestions. In this performance the children were not merely spectators, watching what was going on. They were participants, helping to influence what they saw.

The same thing is happening with the great show that nature is acting out before our eyes. Since we are part of the world of nature, we are not merely spectators of the show—we are participants. By our actions we influence what happens. In fact, we are so deeply involved in the act that even the simplest things we see show the influence of what we ourselves are doing. The theory of relativity shows that this is true even of so simple a thing as measuring a length. If the length of a yardstick depends on how fast it is moving, then any measurements we make will depend on the speed with which we and our yardsticks travel. Another observer, traveling at a different speed, though he measure the same thing we do, will get a different result.

The Elephant and the Blind Men

If two observers, traveling at different speeds, get different measurements for the same object, can they ever agree on the nature of the thing they are measuring? There is an old fable about some blind men who came across an elephant. One felt the tail and decided that an elephant was like a rope. Another felt a leg, and announced that an elephant was like a tree. A third felt the elephant's trunk, and decided that an elephant was like a snake. Are we doomed to be like the blind men, each one of us getting a different view of the world, and never agreeing on its real nature? The answer given by the theory of relativity is "no." While the measurements made by observers may differ, depending on their own motions, they can discover from their measurements characteristics of the physical world that do not depend on their motions at all. These can be figured out with the help of mathematics, and will be the same for all observers.

There is a real world that we learn about through our observations and activities, and especially through our work. Because each man alone can see only a small part of it, his own view of the world is one-sided and incomplete. But if he joins with other men, sharing ideas and experiences, he can see that world from many sides. By piecing together the bits of information contributed by many men of many nations, and accumulated through thousands of years, we gradually build up a more complete picture of the real world.

We differ from the blind men because we don't merely gather personal observations. We combine the observations of many people, and construct theories based on these observations. We test and correct these theories through the work we do and the additional experience we have while we work. A theory which has been tested in this way then serves as a guide for our future actions. If the blind men of the fable had done the same thing, they would soon have learned about the real elephant that was independent of their own one-sided observations. And they would have been able to put the elephant to work for them as the people of India do.

Stopping the Clock

Another strange result following from the theory of relativity is that time measurements are not the same for all observers. Just as scientists had to throw out the idea of a fixed, unchanging measure of length, so they also had to throw out the idea of an abstract flow of time, independent of all real objects. How is time measured? With real clocks, of course, of one kind or another. But every clock is itself an object that moves with a certain rhythm used to count out the intervals of time—seconds, minutes, hours, and so on. Now the rhythm of the clock, like the length of the yard-stick, depends on its own state of motion. To show how this works, let's go back to our old friends, John and Mary. This time they are both carrying clocks; and again, when they start out, they are both moving at the same speed. They compare clocks and find that both clocks are moving with the same rhythm. Again Mary starts moving away from John at a greatly increased speed. John checks her clock against his as she moves away from him and finds that it is moving at a slower rhythm than his own. In fact, the faster Mary moves, the slower her clock runs.

What would happen if Mary moved away from John at the speed of light? The mathematical equations of the theory of relativity give a very curious answer. They say that Mary's clock would slow down to a halt, compared to John's. To John it seems as though time has stopped passing for Mary.

Of course, you don't really believe that, do you? And you're right not to. It's another fantasy and another way in which the equations remind us that it is impossible for anybody ever to move with the speed of light.

Atomic Energy

Remember that we said the mass of a body depends on how fast it is moving. This is another of the strange results of the theory of relativity. You can't verify it by your everyday experience, because the effect of ordinary speeds is too small to be noticed. But scientists have observed the change of mass in small particles traveling at high speeds. In fact, you have learned about one of the effects of this change of mass on the spectra of the elements: The fine structure of the spectrum resulting from the rotation of the orbits of the electrons that surround the nucleus.

The increase in mass of a moving body comes from its energy of motion. It takes a lot of energy to make a small amount of mass. This discovery, that energy can be turned into mass, led to the prediction that the process can be reversed, and that a small amount of mass can be turned into a large amount of energy. This prediction was the foundation of the studies that led to the development of atomic energy.

The Stuff of the Universe

It may seem strange that the speed of one thing alone, the speed of light, should have the privileged position that it does in the theory of relativity. But is it so strange, after all? Our notion of what light is, has been growing with our knowledge. We no longer think of it only as visible light. We broadened the idea to include all electromagnetic radiation. Then we discovered that radiation is only one form in which energy may exist, and that energy may be changed from one form to another. Now, through relativity, we have found that energy can be turned into mass, and mass into energy. But everything in the universe is made of mass and energy. No wonder, then, that the speed of light plays a central role in physical theory. Light is the stuff of which the universe is made!

The Road to Knowledge

Through the ages people have learned more and more about matter—the stuff of the universe. As their knowledge grew, their ideas about matter changed. They once thought that mass and energy were completely separate. Today, science has shown us how mass and energy are connected with each other, how they are but two forms of matter. At the same time, however, scientists keep making new discoveries about matter, especially in their studies of the nucleus of the atom. Now one of their problems is to find out how these new discoveries are related to our present knowledge of the forms of matter. On the basis of past experience it is safe to say that they will solve this problem—but not forever. Each new discovery answers old questions, but at the same time raises new ones. There will always be uncharted regions of the universe to explore.

The Real Hero

This story, like all good stories, has a hero. By this time you have probably guessed who it is—it is man.

Light can travel through empty space, bringing messages from the tiniest atom or the farthest stars at a speed of 186,000 miles per second. But it is man who has tamed light, using instruments like magnets, prisms, lenses, mirrors, gratings, X-ray tubes, and radio circuits to put light to work. In the person of an unknown Chinese inventor thousands of years ago, man created the magnetic compass. In the person of the Dutch optician, Hans Lipperskey, man invented the telescope. As Hans and Zacharias Janssen he invented the microscope. Through Newton he found the spectrum, and through Huyghens and Young he discovered light waves. As Mendeleyev he worked out the periodic table of the elements.

Man is a giant with billions of eyes and billions of hands. His accomplishments are the work of many men, of all nations and many generations. English and Chinese, French, Russians and Dutch, Americans and Italians, all contributed to the discoveries and inventions described in this book. Each investigator used the store of knowledge handed down to him from earliest times, enlarged it by his own work, and then passed it on to future workers right down to our own

day. In this way what man has learned and what he has done are the result of people working together and learning from each other, with each generation standing on the shoulders of the one before. Man is a giant because he does not work alone.

Man is the giant who is slowly but surely conquering light and the other tremendous forces of nature and making them serve his own purposes. He doesn't just take the world as he finds it. He actively changes it to meet his needs. Man, who was born to crawl on land, has taught himself to fly in the air, and sail over and under the sea. Man, who is born naked, without even a coat of fur to protect him, builds shelters of stone and steel that reach up into the sky. Man, whose feeble voice can barely be heard a thousand feet away, speaks to his fellow man on the other side of the earth. He has dammed up floods, watered deserts, and grown food from barren soil. And as he begins to conquer disease and hunger, he is beginning to lengthen his own life.

Science changes along with the changes in the way people live and work. When Newton was making his great discoveries about light, the industrial revolution in England was getting into full swing. Indeed Newton's work helped to speed it up. In the centuries that followed, science became ever more necessary, and new discoveries followed each other hard and fast—Darwin, Mendeleyev, the Curies. Today, with the development of atomic power, mankind stands on the threshold of bigger changes.

Man's knowledge of nature has given him power over nature. Science, however, is not an end in itself, but a tool which people use in the course of their life and work. Atomic energy can be used to destroy a whole city or to make the desert blossom. It all depends on what people do with it. Today, for the first time in history, the great discoveries of the scientists have opened up the possibility of giving all the people in the world enough food, clothing, housing, and medical care.

In order to use this power over nature to the full, men must also learn to understand and control their relations with each other, their social organization. They must find the way to live in peace and work together. Then they can put light to work in many new and wonderful ways which will make the world a rich and splendid place, not just for a few but for all people.

Reading List

Suggested Readings on light and related subjects

Irving Adler, *Color In Your Life,* The John Day Co., New York. *Inside the Nucleus,* The John Day Co., New York. *The Stars: Steppingstones into Space.* The John Day Co., New York.

Max Born, *The Restless Universe,* Dover Publications, New York.

Sir William Bragg, *The Universe of Light,* Dover Publications, New York.

M. Minnaert, *Light and Color in the Open Air,* Dover Publications, New York.

Glossary

Amplitude—The height of a wave.

Angle of incidence—The angle between a ray coming toward a surface and the normal to the surface.

Angle of reflection—The angle between a ray reflected from a surface and the normal to the surface.

Angle of refraction—The angle between a ray refracted by a surface and the normal to the surface.

Atom—The smallest particle of a chemical element.

Atomic number—The number that shows the place of an atom in the periodic table. It is equal to the number of protons in the atom's nucleus.

Bright line spectrum—The spectrum formed from the light emitted by a glowing gas.

Compound microscope—A microscope made of two lenses called the *objective* and the *eye-piece*. The objective forms an enlarged real image of the object being viewed, and the eye-piece forms an enlarged virtual image of this real image.

Concave lens—A lens that is thinner at the center than at the edge.

Convex lens—A lens that is thicker at the center than at the edge.

Critical angle—The angle of incidence at which a ray, after refraction, becomes parallel to the refracting surface.

Dark line spectrum—The spectrum formed from light after some of its colors have been removed or weakened by passage through a gas.

Energy—The capacity to do work.

Focal length—The distance between the center of a lens and a principal focus.

Frequency—The number of crests of a wave that pass a fixed point in one second.

Grating—A surface with closely packed equally spaced parallel lines scratched on it, used to separate the different colors in mixed light.

Infra-red rays—Rays with wavelengths that are longer than the wavelengths of red light but not as long as radio wavelengths. They are also called heat rays.

Interference—The cancellation of some light waves by combining them with others that are out of step with them.

Mirage—A virtual image formed by total reflection at the surface between a superheated layer of air near the ground and the rest of the air above it.

Molecule—The smallest particle of a chemical compound.

Node—A motionless point in a vibrating object.

Normal—A line that is perpendicular to a surface (not leaning toward the surface in any direction).

Nucleus of an atom—The heavy core at the center of the atom.

Optic nerve—The nerve that joins the retina of the eye to the brain.

Photon—The small bundles of energy in a ray of light.

Principal focus—In a convex lens, it is the point to which rays originally parallel will converge after they are refracted by the lens. In a concave lens, it is the point from which rays originally parallel seem to diverge after they are refracted by the lens.

Rainbow—A spectrum formed by the reflection and refraction of light at the surface of small droplets of water in the air.

Real image—An image formed at a place to which light from an object is made to converge.

Reflection—Bouncing back from a smooth surface.

Refraction—The bending of a ray of light.

Retina—The light-sensitive screen at the back of the eye.

Shell of an atom—A set of all electrons surrounding the nucleus that have orbits of about the same size.

Simple microscope—A single convex lens used to form a virtual image that is larger than the object.

Spectrum—The colors in a thin beam of mixed light, separated and arranged side by side in order of increasing wavelength.

Stark effect—The splitting of the lines of the spectrum of an atom by an electric field.

Total reflection—The reflection that takes place when the angle of incidence is larger than the critical angle.

Ultra-violet rays—Rays with wavelengths that are shorter than the wavelengths of violet light but not as short as X-ray wavelengths.

Virtual image—An image of an object at a place where the object seems to be but is not. The object seems to be there because light from the object, after being bent or reflected, seems to be coming from that place.

Wavelength—The distance between two neighboring crests of a wave.

Zeeman effect—The splitting of the lines of the spectrum of an atom by a magnetic field.

Index

About the Author

Teacher, scholar, and author of over four dozen books, Irving Adler writes about *The Story of Light* out of his own fascination with the fact that man's knowledge of atomic structure begins with coded light messages from the atom.

Dr. Adler was born in New York. He was graduated magna cum laude from City College of New York City and holds graduate degrees from Columbia University, where he has also taught. He and his wife live in Shaftsbury, Vermont.

About the Artist

A native of Boston, Anne Lewis studied at the Boston Museum of Fine Arts and was graduated from the Massachusetts School of Art, now known as the Massachusetts College of Art. Now a resident of New York City, Mrs. Lewis has designed and illustrated many children's books. Among them are *Grunion: Fish Out of Water, Shakespeare for Young Players, The Story of Birds of North America, Let's Learn About the Orchestra,* and *Toss and Catch,* which she wrote as well as illustrated.

Cover Photography by Frank Worth